Decisions Involving Uncertainty: An @RISK™ Tutorial for the Petroleum Industry

James A. Murtha

Preface

New Printing

When first printed in 1993, this book referenced earlier versions of @RISK for both Lotus 123 and Excel platforms. Since then, Lotus 123 has significantly dwindled in popularity and both Excel and @RISK have undergone several revisions. The current printing updates all references to @RISK in Excel and omits all references to 123.

In spite of temptations to the contrary, very few other changes have been made to the text. New examples have not been added, even those such as the cost models that have become staples in class. The references have not been updated. Lessons learned from the 200 or so classes and 2000-odd students have not been announced or passed along.

It is the author's intent to do all these other good things in due time and bring forth a new edition, perhaps as early as the year 2002. It is only fair to say, however, that the same time frame (two years) would have been offered as an estimate any time during the past two years. But let us neither dwell on the dreary nor be too amused at the helplessness of the forecast by one who purports to help others in this regard. The present printing should be welcome to many who have not wished to translate the language through the version changes of @RISK or dodge the persistent references to 123. Certainly, the new figures and layout being developed by the able staff at Palisade will be pleasing to the eye.

Where this book came from

This book grew out of the class notes for a course entitled "Monte Carlo Simulation Using @RISK", which premiered in April 1992 and which has been offered primarily to professionals in the oil and gas industry. The participants have been engineers, geologists and geophysicists, planners and economists, managers, and technical support personnel. Over the years, although the typical class was offered in-house for a petroleum company, there have been a dozen or more classes sponsored by the Society of Petroleum Engineers, several classes sponsored by Palisade Corporation, and several classes for cost engineers, the electric power industry, and even NASA. The examples in the book are focused on upstream oil and gas applications.

How to use this book

In its present form, this book could be used as

a) a tutorial for petroleum professionals learning @RISK,

b) a reference book for occasional users of Monte Carlo simulation,

c) a source of simple examples for people interested in designing more complex simulation models.

I imagine that most readers will be sitting at their computers while they browse. There are plenty of examples and exercises to play with. Monte Carlo simulation is not a spectator sport. You get good at it by designing your own models, developing your own worksheets, running simulations, and mulling over the results.

This is an elementary book with a relatively narrow focus.

This is an introductory level book. Examples of material that is beyond the scope of this work include 1) comprehensive models of exploration and production, 2) diagnostics of correlation matrices, 3) curve fitting of historical data, and 4) significance tests. Likewise, there was a conscious effort to specialize in Monte Carlo simulation, at the expense of more general risk analysis or decision analysis. While decision trees are mentioned, they are not discussed in detail. Influence diagrams are not treated. Economics fundamentals are not presented. It is assumed that the reader is familiar with common yardsticks and tools such as discounted cash flow, net present value, rates of return, and the like.

The author assumes no liability for the worksheets provided.

This is the standard caveat you see with software tools. Worksheets provided with this book are not intended to be commercial quality software. Rather, they are suggestions, starting points, building blocks. The author neither assumes any responsibility for their validity nor recommends them to be used for serious application in their present form. Since the vast majority of them have been used as classroom devices, they should be relatively clean. Nevertheless, the process of capturing pictures and responding to editorial suggestions often leads to changes in cell addresses and other minor annoyances. These worksheets are simple.

Having denied any responsibility for the simple models provided, I hasten to invite you, the reader, to tell me what you think about this book, to ask questions, to suggest improvements, and generally to communicate. As the number of @RISK users continues to grow, there is more opportunity to share (generic) ideas and to help each other overcome stumbling blocks.

Acknowledgments

Several people helped greatly with the first printing. Bill Barton, formerly of Palisade Corporation, was supportive and always available as a sounding board. Harvey Lipman, a former teaching colleague, found time to review Chapter 2. I owe a debt of gratitude to the participants in seminars and training classes for asking good questions and sharing their ideas. During 1992 and 1993, I had the chance to work closely with several thought-provoking individuals, especially Curt Killinger, formerly of Texaco. Ned Timbel of GES International, a consulting geologist, and Curt Schneider, an engineer with Conoco, volunteered the ultimate effort of reading everything, working through the examples and problems, and demanding clarity. From big picture to wordsmithing, they stuck with it mercilessly.

Two people played a significant role in both printings. Susan Peterson, formerly of Marathon and Halliburton, now a business associate of mine, read early portions of the first printing and offered her usual sound advice. More recently, she reviewed the current version. Wilton Adams, formerly of Texaco, donned his copy-editing hat, chiding me for substituting minus signs for em-dashes as well as more serious gaffes. Recently as he assisted us in several classes, he continued to find flaws and oversights.

Finally, this printing came about because Sam McLafferty, the able leader of Palisade Corporation, finally convinced me that the benefits of a spiffy, up-to-date version were good value for the collective investment of his staff and those of us who reviewed the manuscript.

As before, I assume ultimate responsibility for this work. Naturally, I would be grateful to hear from all readers

Table of Contents

Chapter 1: Risk Analysis in The Petroleum Industry

This book concentrates on Monte Carlo simulation, a tool used in risk analysis or decision making under uncertainty. To understand risk analysis, one must have a good working definition of risk. This chapter begins by defining the terms *risk* and *uncertainty*, and illustrating the use of these words with examples from everyday situations. Next, we introduce the concept of stochastic models - models that incorporate uncertainty - and contrast them with the deterministic and scenario approaches. Finally, two other decision-making tools are discussed, decision trees and tornado diagrams, which are generally used to supplement, but not replace, Monte Carlo simulation

1.1 What is Risk Analysis?

The words risk and uncertainty will find their way into our discussion frequently. Unfortunately, authors have not agreed on definitions of these terms, especially risk. Indeed, you are more likely to find definitions of "risk preference" or "risk aversion" or "decisions under uncertainty" and other combined forms than you are direct definitions of risk and uncertainty. While it may be easier to provide a careful definition of each term at the end of this book, when we have a fuller understanding of the concepts, we need working definitions now.

1.1.1 Definitions of Risk and Uncertainty

According to Webster's Unabridged New Universal Dictionary,

> **Risk** is "The chance of injury, damage, or loss; the degree of probability of loss, the amount of possible loss."

> **Uncertainty** is "The quality or state of being uncertain, lack of certainty, doubt."

We will use uncertainty and risk to refer to the outcomes - and their implications - of some future event. *Uncertainty* will describe and refer to the range of possible outcomes. *Risk* will be reserved to describe the potential gains or losses associated with particular outcomes.

1.1.2 Examples of Risk and Uncertainty

One example would be for you to spin a wheel having 10 possible stops (numbered 1, 2, ...,10) and win $100 if the pointer stops at the number 7, otherwise lose $10. As you spin the wheel, the exact place where it will stop is *uncertain* and could be any of the 10 possibilities. Assuming the wheel is fair, each of these 10 outcomes is *equally likely*. The probability that the wheel stops at 7 is 1/10. The *uncertainty* has to do with which number will come up. The *risk* to you is that 90% of the time (in the long run) you will lose $10, while 10% of the time you will win $100.

You cannot eliminate the uncertainty of the wheel spin. You can, however, quantify it and describe the risk associated with it. Moreover, you can eliminate the risk to yourself by choosing not to play the game.

It will be convenient to describe the outcomes as well as the gains in terms of *parameters*. A parameter is another word for a variable in some equation; parameters usually either count or measure things.

A Household Budget

As a second example, consider the matter of building a household budget. The various categories (rent or mortgage, food, repairs, utilities, and so on) represent components of the overall budget. These items are the parameters. They are inputs to the budget function. Each month, you must estimate the value of each of the parameters for the upcoming month. Let's consider the difference between paying next month's rent (or mortgage payment) and paying next month's electric utility bill. Generally, you know how much the rent will be, but you can only estimate your electric bill. The exact value of your bill is uncertain.

To capture the notion of risk, suppose you are operating on a tight budget and set aside some money for your electric bill, say $120, knowing that if the bill exceeds that amount, you will have to reduce the budget in some other area, such as entertainment. You are taking some risk that the bill will be greater than $120. If you are cautious, you will typically set aside enough money to make it highly unlikely or improbable that the actual amount of the bill exceeds your estimate. While this may be an appealing philosophy, the extra cash you didn't need for the electric bill could have been spent on something else.

You may have noticed that we have already introduced some familiar words that are charged with meaning: estimate, actual, risk, unlikely, improbable. We have begun to explore the language of probability, statistics, and risk analysis.

The value of the upcoming electric bill is unknown. The budgeted amount is your estimate of that unknown quantity. From your household records, you can estimate the value of the bill. This estimation process may be simple, such as taking the average value of the last few months' bills, or taking last year's bill for the same month. Alternatively, we can make the estimate more complicated by incorporating such factors as the weather forecast, usage changes, visiting house guests who are couch potatoes and watch television all day, a more efficient heating/air condition system, new insulation, inflation, changes in utility rate, and so on.

When the bill arrives, its value becomes known, and your estimate is either adequate or not. Consequently, the penalty is either extracted or not: you get an extra video rental or you forego the trip to the beach. In short, the case is closed, at least until the next budget is constructed, at which time you may be influenced by the outcome of this process.

An Exploration Prospect

As a third example, we look at a routine analysis done on a corporate level. Before an exploration prospect is undertaken, someone usually has to estimate the various costs and expenses along with potential benefits, such as the value of the asset. Moreover, it is useful to propose a schedule of investment and production, and several measures of success that allow for comparison with competing projects. Estimating the rent may be analogous to estimating the lease payment and certain other fixed costs. Estimating the utility bill may be analogous to estimating the operating expenses for a single oil well for a year. Your educated estimate of operating expenses may be $120,000/yr. To arrive at that estimate, you might start with a survey of operational costs for other wells your company has operated recently. In this case you would also take a hard look at the trends in the cost of services, the level of operational usage, and changes in the environment (weather, political climate, economic climate).

If your estimate falls short, the penalty may be a reduction in anticipated profit for the project. There may also be some impact on the careers of the engineers and planners involved such as raises, reassignments, promotions.

All three of these examples represent risk analysis. The only things that set apart the household budget matter from the planning specialist in the oil industry are 1) the scale of the numbers, 2) the significance of the penalties, 3) the implications to you as a decision-maker or advisor to the decision makers.

Both of the budget examples focus on upcoming events (e.g., receipt of invoices), involving some quantitative measure (e.g., the electric bill, the annual operating expenses). There is historical data (e.g., previous invoices) which can be quantified (e.g., find the minimum, the maximum, the most likely range), but the exact value of the measure is uncertain. Your job is to estimate the unknown value. There are some disadvantages to a poor estimate. Underestimating may mean a shortfall of cash for other planned activities. Overestimating may mean loss of an opportunity for other investments. Risk is the potential loss or gain and its consequences associated with an estimate of some future unknown event. Generally, describing the range of possible outcomes - and their consequences - is the objective of the risk analysts.

To repeat, you cannot eliminate uncertainty. You can only attempt to describe it. An appropriate answer to the question, "How much will next month's electric bill be?" is "The bill will be between $100 and $160. It is more likely to be less than $120, rather than more than $120. There is only a 5% chance that the bill will exceed $140."

1.1.3 Why Do Risk Analysis?

Risk analysis is a future-oriented activity. We are trying to forecast or predict events yet to come. We are attempting to quantify the unknown. One of the principal reasons for this activity is to compare alternative investments. Corporations, banks, and investors all have an interest in the potential benefits of each investment they consider. If you invest $10,000 in a certificate of deposit, you know what you will get in return. That same investment in the stock market carries uncertainty. You may lose money or you may gain.

Investing in a drilling prospect or a waterflood prospect is a *risky* undertaking. Before you invest, you want some idea of the potential outcomes and their value to you. Then you can assess the risk. The risk analysts combine the principles of probability and statistics with sources of data and expert opinion to try to quantify the uncertainty and risk associated with an investment opportunity.

Whenever an oil and gas property is sold or transferred, someone has to assign a value to it. A property that has produced 23,000 barrels of oil in its first five years has potential for future production as well as future expenses (royalties, operations, workovers, plugging). Together these components make up the present value of the well. An engineer can examine the production history and make a production forecast, which can be converted into an economics forecast. If that engineer is familiar with the principles of risk analysis, he or she could provide forecasts that accommodate uncertainty. Thus, rather than predicting 1250 barrels of production next year, the production forecast might be "...between 1000 and 1400 barrels of oil, with 1250 the most likely case, and a 10% chance of producing less than 1100 barrels.". You get the idea. That is what this book is all about.

One of the main uses of risk analysis is to compare two or more alternative investments opportunities within a corporation or for investors. Which investment has the greater risk? Which one has the greater potential for return on investment? Planning the budget involves selecting a few projects among several competing possibilities. Informed decisions require analysis of the ranges of possible outcomes and their implications.

Who should know about risk analysis? Certainly bankers, lawyers, planners, investors, engineers, geophysicists, geologists, managers, economists, regulatory industry personnel. In short, anyone who is involved in decisions regarding investments, management, partnership, or transfer of ownership has reason to become acquainted with the principles of risk analysis.

1.2 Models in the Oil and Gas Industry

Most of us approach risk analysis from a disciplinary perspective. Explorationists want to quantify the uncertainty associated with finding hydrocarbons. They concentrate on basin analysis or play analysis. For a given prospect, they estimate the likelihood of an adequate reservoir and trap, and the proximity of thermally mature source material. Later they estimate reserves and the associated cash flows. Drilling engineers want to examine historic data hoping not only to estimate normal drilling costs, but also to quantify the risk of stuck pipe, blowouts, lost circulation, and other problems encountered while drilling a well. Reservoir and production engineers simulate field sizes, productivity indices, decline rates, prices, and development and operational costs. They work with exploration and drilling team members to estimate schedules and the amount of capital investment (drilling, platforms, pipelines, etc.) required. Public utility companies who transport natural gas are concerned with demand and supply matters and the probability of experiencing peak load as well as prices and costs.

In addition to differences between disciplines, there are significant situational differences. Drilling engineers in the Gulf Coast worry about different matters than their counterparts in other geographic locations. Explorationists in offshore environments are constrained by platform facilities options, water depth, and shipping lanes. Reservoir and production engineers interested in gas from coal seams care more about adsorption capacity than hydrocarbon pore volume estimates. What all these people share when they engage in risk analysis is a methodology that replaces a number with a probability distribution. When we restrict our models so that each parameter takes on only one value, we call the model deterministic. When we allow parameters to be represented by random variables or probability distributions, however, the models are known as stochastic or probabilistic (both words refer to uncertainty). The contrast between these two approaches can be seen clearly by introducing an intermediate step, which we will call the scenario approach.

Let us take the universal problem of the volumetric estimate of reserves. We use a simplified equation:

$$N = A * h * R \tag{1.1}$$

where A is the area in acres, h is the net pay in ft, and R is a recovery factor (in STB/ac-ft or Mscf/ac-ft) which accounts for conversion of units, porosity, oil saturation, formation volume factor and recovery efficiency.

1.2.1 The Deterministic Approach

Suppose our best estimates for A, h and R happen to be 300 ac, 25 ft, and 200 STB/ac-ft. Then our best estimate for reserves is 1.5 MMSTB. This is a deterministic statement. It doesn't tell us anything about the likelihood that the reserves might be less than 1.0 MMSTB or greater than 2.0 MMSTB, for example. In other words, all we can say is that our most likely estimate is 1.5 MMSTB. Figure 1.1 illustrates the simplistic nature of this approach.

Figure 1.1 Deterministic Example Showing Single Value Inputs and Single Output

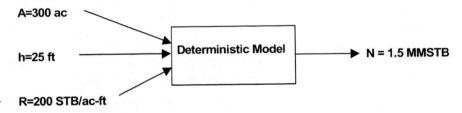

1.2.2 The Scenario Approach

An improved method is to establish the worst, most likely, and best case scenarios. Thus, we could assign to each parameter three values, and calculate three values for reserves, according to the following table. The process is also illustrated in Figure 1.2.

Table 1.1 Input and Output Data for Scenario Model

Parameter / units		Worst	Most Likely	Best
A	ac	150	300	450
h	ft	15	25	35
R	STB/ac-ft	100	200	300
Reserves , MMSTB		0.225	1.5	4.725

What have we learned? If nothing else, considering these three possibilities, we become aware of the range of possibilities for reserves. The natural questions arise: How likely are the worst and best scenarios?. More to the point, **How likely is the most likely case?** Would we expect it to happen less than a third of the time?

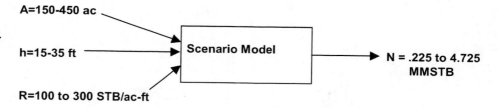

Figure 1.2 Schematic Diagram for Scenario Model

A=150-450 ac

h=15-35 ft

R=100 to 300 STB/ac-ft

Scenario Model

N = .225 to 4.725 MMSTB

Putting aside for now two serious questions - Where did we obtain the estimates for the three cases? and How reliable are they? Several other questions come to mind. At what point are the reserves too small to be attractive? What is the likelihood (probability) that the reserves would be at least as large as our cutoff value? What is the likelihood that reserves will be at least as large as our most likely estimate? The scenario method, unfortunately, fails to give us answers to the questions like the last two. We have no mechanism for describing the possibilities of outcomes between the three scenario cases of worst, best, and most likely. That is where the stochastic method can help us out.

1.2.3 The Stochastic Approach

With the stochastic approach to risk analysis, we want to treat each parameter as a random variable. For instance, we could say that A is a normally distributed random variable with mean 300 ac and standard deviation 50 ac, and that h is normally distributed with mean 25 ft and standard deviation of 5 ft. Likewise the recovery factor is uniformly distributed over the range of 100 to 300 STB/ac-ft.

Now the calculation of the estimates for reserves becomes more complicated. In fact, until the emergence of computers, this method was tedious. Without going into all the details, we have to perform Monte Carlo simulation. In brief, we randomly select one value from each of these three variables, take their product to get one estimate of reserves, and then repeat the process hundreds or thousands of times, while storing all the results. Moreover, if there is reason to believe that there is dependency among the parameters, then it is necessary to adjust the sampling process to account for it. When we finish, we display the results in the form of a histogram. Finally, we can answer the questions posed above. We can estimate the probability that the reserves will be at least as large as any given value. We can estimate the probability that reserves falls into a given range of values. Figure 1.3 summarizes the process.

*Figure 1.3
Diagram of a
Simple Monte
Carlo
Simulation
Showing
Four Input
Distributions
and One
Output*

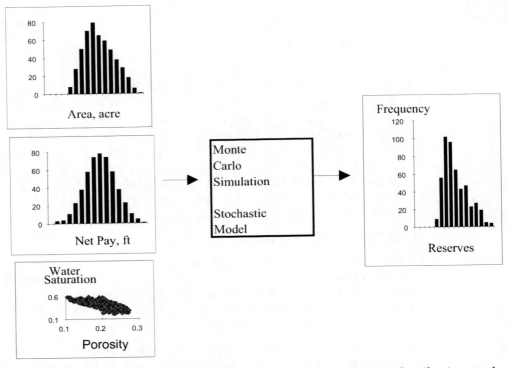

Up to this point, we have not addressed how we obtain the distributions, who decides what would be a representative range of possible values for A, h, and R, or why we should choose a normal distribution rather than a uniform distribution. These issues are extremely important and without addressing them, the Monte Carlo simulation has little bearing on the actual problem we are trying to solve. Another issue that must be addressed in Monte Carlo simulation is whether any of the input parameters are *dependent* on one another. In Chapter 2 we offer some methods of obtaining appropriate distributions and suggest ways to estimate the extent to which there is correlation between pairs of variables.

To report the result of calculation from the deterministic model, we merely provide a number for reserves or N. To report the calculation (i.e., a simulation) for a stochastic model, we would provide a histogram of the results. Learning how to incorporate probability distributions for the parameters in our models, how to run simulations, and how to interpret the results is the essence of the risk analysis we will study.

**Models -
The Key to
Different
Disciplines**

The simple equation we have used to illustrate different methods of estimating reserves is an example of a *model* - typically in the form of one or more equations coupled with fundamental assumptions which provide a representation of some physical reality. Technical people rely on models, regardless of the discipline. Some models are more rigorous, more closely aligned with fundamental principles, while others are more heuristic in nature and are based on large quantities of data that seem to follow a pattern. What many models have in common is that they require input values for the parameters in their equations. These estimates, like the case we just described, can be deterministic (single point estimates) or stochastic (represented by random variables and their probability distributions).

The following outline offers a glimpse of the myriad of possibilities available to those who wish to incorporate risk analysis into their models.

1.2.4 Exploration Risk

Geologic Risks - Is there hydrocarbon there?

In the case of a structural trap prospect, probabilities can be assigned to each of the following parameters. Often, these parameters are not risked and unlike other models in this book, each of these variables is assigned a single, most likely, value. The reason for assigning a single value is that usually very little information is available at the time when the estimates are made. Nevertheless, risk is often useful in frontier areas, because the assessment may help us decide where to spend more money to obtain more information. The combined probability (of a productive reservoir) is taken to be a product of several of these individual numbers.

- Existence of trap

- Source rock

- Thermal maturation

- Migration and timing

- Reservoir (storage capacity)

- Seals

- Productivity

The *model* would be the following equation:

$$\text{Prob of Hydrocarbon accumulation} = (\text{Prob of Trap}) * (\text{Prob of Source}) * \ldots (\text{Prob of Productivity}) \qquad (1.2)$$

Will the Wells Hit Their Targets?

Risks during drilling are among the concerns of explorationists as well as the drilling engineers. From the explorationists point of view, the principal questions might not be related to drilling. What is the expected drilling success rate in this basin? How can we use the data from the first few wells to revise our estimates of whether a prospect will be drilled easily?

1.2.5 Drilling Risk

In recent years, drilling engineers have begun to acquire and analyze historic data hoping to quantify the risk of stuck pipe, blowouts, lost circulation, and other problems encountered while drilling a well. They have always been involved in some way with projected costs to drill a well, the Authorization for Expenditure (AFE). They separate their costs into two categories, reflecting expected costs and contingency: planned costs and problems. They also include a category called Change of Scope to account for expenses attributed to targets and activities decided upon while the well was being drilled, which went beyond the original target and drilling plan. Naturally, they also acknowledge the important variable of location.

Normal (Planned) Costs

Key variables associated with planned drilling costs are

- Water depth
- Proposed total depth
- Mud program
- Casing program
- Maximum hole angle
- True vertical depth
- Abnormally pressured zones
- Minimum hole size

One approach would be to examine historical data and look for a relationship of the form

$$\text{Cost} = c_0 * X^a * Y^b * Z^c \dots \tag{1.3}$$

where X, Y, Z, ... refer to water depth, total depth, maximum mud weight, and so on. This approach would use multiple regression (on the logarithms of X,Y,Z,...) to estimate the parameters c_0 and a, b, c,.... Like our simple reserves model, we could assign random variables to the input parameters, X,Y,Z, - generating the distributions from historical data. This rather simple approach ignores the possible dependency among the variables, which might interfere with the regression analysis.

General Problem Costs

One common form of problem is stuck pipe. Key variables in estimating the probability of stuck pipe might be

- Water depth
- Hole angle
- Hole size
- Mud weight

The model here might be similar to the regression model for normal costs.

Other problems include blowouts, lost circulation, various equipment problems, lost time waiting for supplies, and cement problems.

Problems Associated with Drilling Locale

Perhaps the most prevalent concern about a new drilling location is accessibility. Imagine the time that went into planning for the first offshore platforms or the pioneering work conducted before drilling in the North Sea and Alaska. Given the levels of uncertainty, some of the modeling must have involved stochastic variables. Problems ranging from poison gas to environmental pollutants can be encountered in particular locations. Major spills and leaks make national headlines. Even seemingly minor problems can cause extensive delays and budget overruns. An example of a highly specialized risk that occurs in offshore environments is collision between ships and drilling vessels. More than 30 collisions occurred between ships and offshore installations prior to 1990. Numerous technical papers have been devoted to this subject. This is a case of tiny probability with devastating consequences. We will not discuss any of these models, but a good reference for the ship collision issue is Spouge (1991).

1.2.6 Production Risk

Field Size The classic volumetric equation for estimating the size of a hydrocarbon (in this case oil) accumulation at a given location is

$$\text{Oil-in-place} = 7758 A h \phi (1 - S_w) / B_o \qquad (1.4)$$

We have already used a simpler variation of this by including a recovery efficiency and lumping together everything except A and h into Recovery, R to get Reserves:

$$\text{Reserves} = AhR \qquad (1.1)$$

Moreover, we may wish to estimate these parameters for each prospect within a basin or play. For instance, if each prospect represents a structure in a basin, we could assign individual probability distributions to each parameter in each structure.

A related issue is the sequence in which the prospects are drilled. This order affects the timing for proving up the reserves and the operational costs. This portion of the modeling overlaps with Drilling and Exploration Risks.

Finally, we could model secondary or improved recovery and take into account several parameters such as costs of infill drilling, facilities, materials, and incremental production. While revenue from this incremental production could be quite significant, the revenue is realized far into the future. Not only is the uncertainty (of prices and expenses, for example) broadened, but the present value of the revenue and costs are substantially reduced by time.

Caldwell and Heather (1991) presented two alternative models for estimating reserves in less conventional settings: coalbed methane reservoirs and naturally fractured reservoirs penetrated by a horizontal well.

In the case of a coalbed methane prospect, they presented these key variables:

- Area (A)
- Net pay (h)
- Gas content (C)
- Density (d)
- Recovery factor (R)

The *model* used for these reserves bears a striking similarity to Equation 1.4.

$$\text{Reserves} = AhCdR \tag{1.5}$$

In the case of a horizontal well in a naturally fractured reservoir, they chose a similar model that incorporated

- Fracture spacing
- Storativity and matrix-to-fracture replenishment capability
- Fracture recovery
- Horizontal wellbore length
- Fracture depletion
- Water saturation

In both of these cases, the underlying model yields a reserve estimate that is simply a **product** of several input variables. These product models have a great deal in common. Differences in the type of distribution (uniform, triangular, normal, lognormal) selected for the input parameters leads to somewhat predictable differences in the outputs. In all cases, the distribution of reserves tends to have a *lognormal* shape - a phenomenon that has a basis in statistical theory. An in-depth discussion of the lognormal distribution can be found in Aitchison and Brown(1957).

Production Forecast

Once recoverable reserves are estimated, we need to estimate how quickly the oil or gas can be produced. Key factors include

- Number of wells
- Percent of dry holes or success ratio
- Drainage area or recovery per well
- Productivity index per well
- Operating constraints on production rates
- Initial decline rates
- Abandonment rates or other abandonment conditions
- Prices of products

One of the more common production forecasting models is the *exponential decline curve*.

$$q = q_i e^{(-at)}$$ (1.6)

This deterministic model can be converted to a stochastic model by treating the two parameters, q_i and a, which represent initial production and decline rate, as probability distributions rather than simply fixed values. Figure 1.4 illustrates how the usual deterministic decline curve gives rise to a range of possibilities. The top curve represents a best case scenario; the bottom, a worst case and the middle curve is the most likely scenario.

Figure 1.4 Probabilistic Forecast of Production Decline for an Oil Well

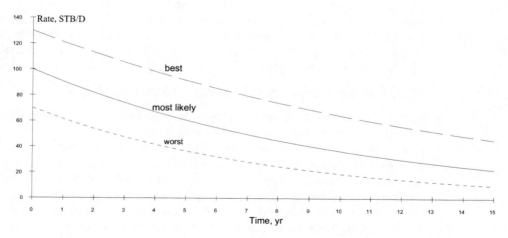

Development Costs, Scheduling, and Production Expenses	There are numerous factors that govern exploration and development of an oil or gas field:

There are numerous factors that govern exploration and development of an oil or gas field:

- Bidding and lease costs
- Drilling costs
- Dry hole costs
- Completion costs
- Scheduling of drilling and construction
- Gas recycling/pressure maintenance needs
- Water disposal
- Maintenance

And for offshore fields,

- Platform and subsea facilities costs
- Pipeline and surface facility requirements

1.3 Other Decision Analysis Tools

Although we will concentrate on Monte Carlo simulation, there are other tools for making decisions, including decision trees and tornado diagrams. Sometimes it is illuminating to apply another methodology in addition to Monte Carlo simulation. Indeed, sometimes decisions don't require the power of Monte Carlo methods. This section offers a glimpse of some tried and true procedures to help in describing a problem, interpreting the results, or testing assumptions. We compare decision trees to Monte Carlo simulation and we use tornado charts to perform help with sensitivity analysis for a simulation.

1.3.1 Decision Trees and Expected Monetary Value

A *decision tree* is a diagram composed of *nodes* and *branches*. There are three types of nodes, *choice* nodes, *chance* nodes, and *terminal* nodes. A choice node represents a *decision* based on rules, often simply reduced to "select the path with the maximum expected gain or the minimum expected loss." A *chance* node represents an uncertain event. Chance nodes are usually depicted as a finite set of mutually exclusive alternatives, each having a prescribed probability of occurrence. Alternatively, a chance node could be represented by a probability distribution. A *terminal* node represents the end of a sequence of branches through chance and choice nodes. Typically, a terminal node is assigned a value representing the last step, from a choice or chance. Figure 1.5 illustrates the three types of nodes in the context of a simplified drilling prospect.

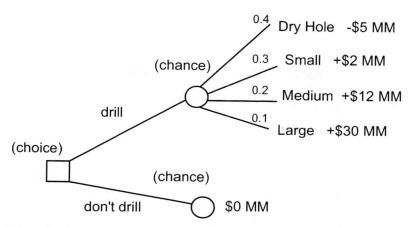

Figure 1.5 Decision Tree for Two-choice Drilling Prospect

Here the choice would be based on the expected value of the two possible decisions: to drill or not to drill. The *expected (monetary) value (EV)* is defined to be the *weighted average* of the monetary estimates of each outcome with its probability. Thus the expected value of drilling would be

$$EV(drill) = 0.4(-5) + 0.3(2) + 0.2(12) + 0.1(30) \qquad \textbf{(1.8)}$$
$$= \$4\text{MM}$$

Since this sum exceeds the (don't-drill) alternative of $0MM, we would choose the drill option. We would reach the opposite conclusion, for example, if the cost of a dry hole were estimated at $15MM, or if the probability of a dry hole were 0.7.

Decision trees like this offer a sensible thought process for planners of large scale projects. As we will see later on, decision trees also offer a means of estimating the value of additional information. To be effective, however, the tree must incorporate sufficient components and have reasonably accurate estimates of both monetary outcomes and probabilities. Where do these two ingredients come from?

The decision tree has only a finite number of identifiable outcomes, each of which requires an estimate for the likelihood of its occurrence as well as an estimate of the value (profit or loss) of that eventuality. As we shall see, the same challenge faces us when we begin a Monte Carlo simulation design. On the surface, the Monte Carlo parameter estimation is more demanding, since we must estimate the shapes of the input distributions for the parameters such as area, pay, initial productivity, porosity, decline rate, and so on. Chapter 3 explores the issues of finding and incorporating historical data, the key steps to estimating these parameters.

**Figure 1.6
Complex
Decision
Tree for
Exploration
Prospect**

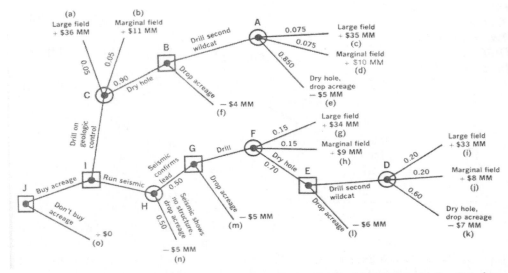

(Used by permission. Source: Paul D Newendorp's *Decision Analysis for Petroleum Exploration.* Copyright PennWell Books, 1975)

Decision trees can get quite complex. Figure 1.6, taken from Newendorp (1975), has 15 terminal nodes, and five each of chance and choice nodes. Generally, moving from left to right in a decision tree corresponds to moving forward in time. The procedure for solving a decision tree requires stepping from right to left, replacing each chance node with its EV and replacing each choice node with the more attractive alternative. In the end, we assign a value to the initial decision, representing the choice of the branch emanating from that node, which has the maximum profit or the least loss.

To give you an idea of the potential complexity, just imagine a decision tree that tried to take into account all the following decision points for each of several appraisal wells.

- run a seismic survey?
- conduct a drill-stem test or run an RFT?
- set intermediate casing?
- obtain fluid samples and do analysis?
- cut core?
- buy more acreage?
- seek a partner?

1.3 Other Decision Analysis Tools

1.3.2 Relationship Between Decision Trees and Monte Carlo Simulation

There are similarities and differences between decision tree analysis and Monte Carlo simulation analysis. For the most part, decision trees and Monte Carlo simulation are alternative methods for analyzing a problem such as an investment decision. Decision trees are graphic by nature and offer a good overview of some complex decisions. Sometimes a decision tree can help clarify or even define a problem in great detail. The chance nodes of a decision tree are, in effect, scenarios. An uncertain event is modeled as a finite set of possible outcomes, each being assigned a probability of occurrence. We could replace each chance node with a probability distribution. Then that component event would be modeled just the way it would be for a Monte Carlo simulation. The output for the decision tree, however, is simply the expected value of that probability distribution, whereas in Monte Carlo simulation, the output would remain a distribution.

Likewise, the final result of a decision tree is a combination of an expected value (not a distribution) and a decision for action. In our example, the solution to the decision tree in Figure 1.5 is $4MM along with the decision to drill. Monte Carlo simulation answers do not include a decision, but rather present ranges of possible outcomes and their likelihoods for various intermediate and bottom line variables. Typical outcomes of a Monte Carlo simulation for an exploration/production decision problem would be distributions for reserves, projections of possible well production profiles, estimates on the number of wells that need to be drilled, and perhaps some economic indicators. The principle decision associated with this simulation – whether to invest in the prospect – is left to those who examine the simulation outputs.

The rule for a decision is straightforward in a decision tree. The largest value (or in some cases, the minimum cost) among the branches is selected. Such simplicity comes from using only the expected values of the alternative paths. In case the path represents a chance node where a distribution of outcomes is known, the decision rules get more complicated. Now we enter the arena of risk preferences. Is the decision maker risk averse or risk-taking? Monte Carlo simulation generally yields more complex descriptions of alternative investments. It may not be prudent to discard all that information and rely solely on the expected value.

1.3.3 Tornado Diagrams

A *tornado diagram or chart* is a device used with stochastic models that illustrates the degree to which a function (the output) is influenced by each of its parameters. Thus, a tornado diagram is a form of *sensitivity analysis*. Consider the reserves model

$$\text{Reserves} = A * h * R \tag{1.1}$$

For sake of argument, suppose we use the same estimates for each of the input parameters – A, h, and R – that we used earlier in this chapter when we talked about the scenario approach (see Table 1.1).

We know that the extreme values of reserves are 0.225 MMSTB and 4.725 MMSTB. To achieve such extremes, however, we must have the corresponding extremes for each input variable occur simultaneously. Instead, let us find what happens when we fix two of the three input parameters at their most likely values while the third input varies from one extreme to the other. First, varying A while fixing h and R, we calculate two cases:

$$\text{Reserves} = 150 * 25 * 200 = 0.75 \text{MMSTB}$$

$$\text{Reserves} = 450 * 25 * 200 = 2.25 \text{MMSTB}$$

Similarly, by varying h with A and R fixed, and then varying R with A and h fixed we get two more pairs of values:

$$\text{Reserves} = 300 * 15 * 200 = 0.90 \text{MMSTB}$$

$$\text{Reserves} = 300 * 35 * 200 = 2.10 \text{MMSTB}$$

and

$$\text{Reserves} = 300 * 25 * 100 = 0.75 \text{MMSTB}$$

$$\text{Reserves} = 300 * 25 * 300 = 2.25 \text{MMSTB}$$

Figure 1.7 Tornado Chart for Simple Reserves Model

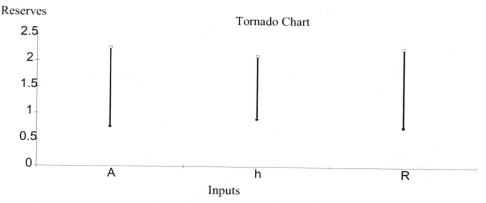

The tornado chart summarizing these values is shown in Figure 1.7. Normally, these charts are presented with the bars horizontal. The tornado chart gets its name from the general shape obtained when the parameters are rearranged so that the most influential ones are at the top of the chart. In the present case, all three input parameters have nearly identical results on the output (reserves). On the one hand, this example does not offer a very dramatic illustration of a tornado chart. On the other hand, the picture tells us that the output (reserves) is equally sensitive the all three inputs. Figure 1.8 illustrates the tornado chart for a more complex model dealing with coalbed methane reserves estimation. Here you can see which parameters have great impact on the bottom line.

Figure 1.8 Tornado Chart for Coalbed Methane Reserves

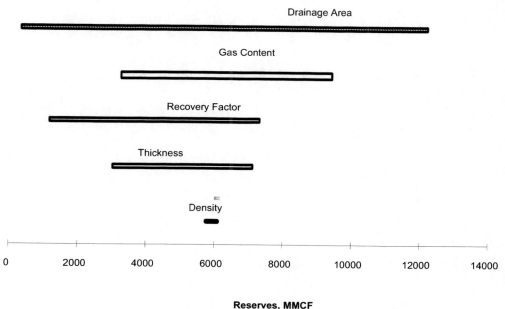

Chapter 2: Probability Distributions – a Basis for Monte Carlo Simulation

This chapter begins with a discussion of how to organize and describe data. Then we examine four theoretical distributions (binomial, normal, lognormal, and triangular). Why these distributions? Because they are simple and widely applicable in and out of the oil and gas industry, and they offer some interesting comparisons. Often we try to impose the shape of some common distribution on a sample of actual data. We say things like "Porosities are normally distributed with a mean of 18% and a standard deviation of 3%." or   "Net pay is uniformly distributed over the range 30 to 45 ft." and we try to select a distribution that fits the data best.

Descriptive statistics and the related probability theory rely on graphic representations of data. Three types of graphs are commonly used and will be reviewed in this chapter, histograms, cumulative distribution functions (CDF's), and probability density functions (PDF's). We construct a histogram to describe a set of 40 porosity values after we group the data into nonoverlapping classes. Alternatively, we represent this same data with a cumulative frequency function. Finally, when we introduce common random variables, like normal, triangular, uniform, and lognormal, we represent them with probability density functions.

Before discussing Monte Carlo simulation, we need to become familiar with some of the language of probability and statistics: sample, random variable, mean, mode, median, standard deviation, and variance. Our primary objective is to achieve adequate familiarity with these concepts so that we may use probability distributions in place of numbers in our models. To replace the value 250 ac with a lognormal distribution having mean 250 and standard deviation 50 ac requires that 1) we understand lognormal distributions and 2) have some evidence from historic data that area is approximately lognormally distributed.

2.1 Some Basic Concepts of Descriptive Statistics

Let's suppose there are records – either in file folders or on a database – for 40 wells in the Lovett field, completed in the Hancock formation. For each well, we have some data: lease name, location, spud date, elevation, wellbore mechanical diagram, measured depth, depth to top and bottom of formation, perforation depths, porosity, water saturation, and so on.

Incidentally, one of the practical problems we face is that these data might be stored in two or three databases or stored in two or three locations. For example, there may be a petrophysical database, a production database, and a reservoir database for the same field. Worse yet, there are likely to be some inconsistencies between the different sources. Who has responsibility for maintenance of a database is a significant company policy matter. There is a larger issue involving where to start looking for historical data, how to validate it, whether the data is adequate and appropriate. Unfortunately, you will not find many answers to those questions in this book. Only as more people begin to rely on Monte Carlo techniques for decision making will we have the means and motivation to address these issues.

For the time being, suppose you have access to all the data. Early this morning, your boss said that she is considering drilling into the Hancock in a new lease and asked you to find out all you can about porosity in the Hancock. What do you do? You might begin with some descriptive statistics as follows.

2.1.1 Samples and Populations

You remember the Lovett Field well data. You dig out all the 40 porosity values. Each porosity itself represents some kind of *average* of the calculated (from electric log data) porosities for the logged interval. These 40 numbers are a *sample* from the *population,* consisting of all possible porosities from all possible penetrations in the Hancock. If you're lucky, these 40 numbers are representative of the population as a whole. This assumption, by the way, underlies nearly everything we do from here on out. We will *infer* characteristics of the larger population based on its sampled subset.

2.1.2 Descriptive Statistics

Putting aside for the moment the matter of how representative these 40 numbers are, you have the task of summarizing the data in a way that your boss might want. Here are some options you might consider.

- Tabulate the 40 porosities in a column on a yellow pad and pop the page into interoffice mail.

- Rearrange the numbers from smallest to largest, calculate the difference between these extremes. This difference is the *range* of the data.

- Calculate the *arithmetic average* or *mean* of the 40 values: add them and divide by 40.

- Group the data into eight equally spaced *classes* ranging from minimum to maximum.

- Plot the grouped data in a *histogram*.

- Plot the *cumulative distribution function* for the data.

Procedures like these make up *descriptive statistics*. With the help of a spreadsheet program, you enter the data, rearrange it from smallest to biggest, group it into categories, and build two graphs for it: frequency histogram and cumulative distribution function. Table 2.1 shows the original data in the order you retrieved it, along with the sorted data allowing you to find the median. Table 2.2 shows the grouped data with the tallies for frequency and cumulative frequency.

The terminology is straightforward. A *class* is defined as an interval on a number scale such as

"greater than 0.064 but less than or equal to 0.086."

The *class boundaries* are the endpoints of the interval, 0.064 and 0.086. The *frequency* is the number of data points falling into the class. *Cumulative frequencies* are assigned to each class by taking a running total beginning with the frequency for the first class and adding subsequent frequencies.

Figure 2.1 shows the histogram corresponding to the grouping in Table 2.2. The main rules for histograms are that 1) all classes have the same width and 2) each datum falls into exactly one class. Figure 2.2 shows the cumulative distribution function (CDF). The CDF, which plays a significant role in Monte Carlo simulation, uses class boundaries for X and cumulative frequencies for Y.

Table 2.1
Unsorted
and Sorted
Porosities
for 40 Wells
in the
Hancock
Zone of the
Lovett field

Porosities from 40 wells				Sorted porosities			
0.161	0.161	0.134	0.109	0.065	0.121	0.154	0.183
0.112	0.197	0.154	0.183	0.077	0.131	0.160	0.183
0.149	0.196	0.196	0.145	0.082	0.134	0.161	0.194
0.169	0.149	0.111	0.065	0.086	0.134	0.161	0.196
0.110	0.082	0.134	0.160	0.096	0.145	0.168	0.196
0.207	0.103	0.169	0.208	0.103	0.146	0.169	0.197
0.146	0.168	0.153	0.194	0.109	0.149	0.169	0.207
0.131	0.086	0.096	0.183	0.110	0.149	0.176	0.208
0.121	0.230	0.176	0.077	0.111	0.149	0.177	0.210
0.179	0.210	0.177	0.149	0.112	0.153	0.179	0.230

Table 2.2
Grouped
Data:
Porosities
of 40 Wells
in the
Hancock
Zone of the
Lovett Field

Class	Frequency	Cumulative Frequency	XY for CDF X	Y
			0.064	0
> 0.064 to 0.086	4	4	0.086	4
> 0.086 to 0.108	2	6	0.108	6
> 0.108 to 0.130	5	11	0.130	11
> 0.130 to 0.152	8	19	0.152	19
> 0.152 to 0.174	8	27	0.174	27
> 0.174 to 0.196	6	33	0.196	33
> 0.196 to 0.218	6	39	0.218	39
> 0.218 to 0.240	1	40	0.240	40

In the spirit of descriptive statistics, we record some facts about these data (definitions will follow):

Minimum value = 0.065

Maximum value = 0.230

Range: 0.230-0.065 = 0.165 (Some people say the range is 0.065 to 0.230)

Median from raw data = (0.153+0.154)/2 = 0.1535

Mode of grouped data = tie: classes 0.130 to 0.152 and 0.152 to 0.174 (both classes contain 8 data)

Figure 2.1 Histogram of Grouped Data Porosity from the Hancock Zone, Lovett Field

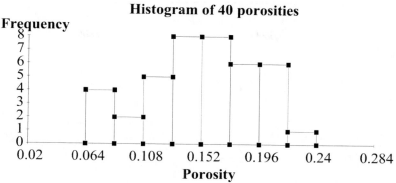

Histogram of 40 porosities

Figure 2.2 CDF for Grouped Porosity Data from the Hancock Formation

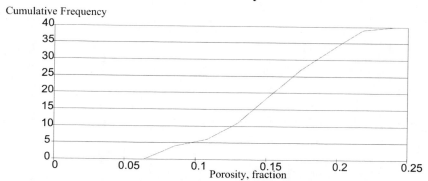

2.2 The Bare Bones of Probability and Statistics

Probability theory is a branch of pure mathematics. It provides a foundation for statistics, which is a subject that cuts across numerous disciplines such as psychology, economics, education, engineering, and the health professions, as well as mathematics. Statistics tends to be pragmatic, very applied in nature. In a university, courses in probability are taught primarily in the math department, but statistics classes are taught in several departments, allowing students to focus only on the methods most applicable to their particular interests.

Our immediate goal is to review some fundamentals of both probability and statistics, to learn some definitions, to encounter several examples of distributions, and to master some simple calculation procedures. Many of the words we define should look familiar to you.

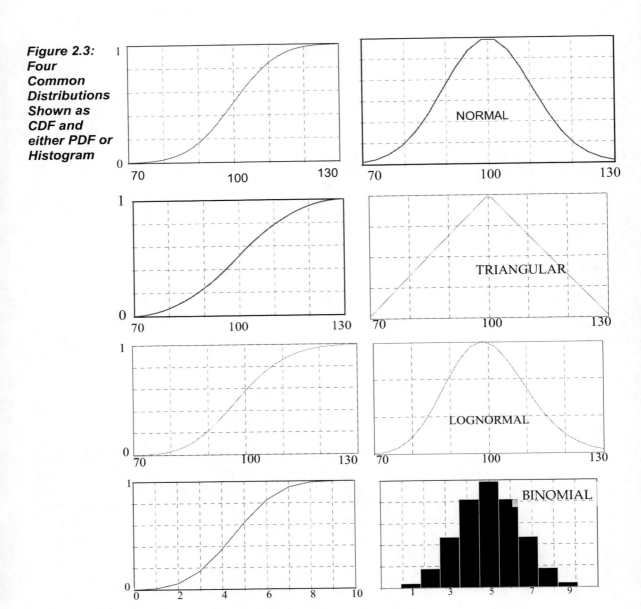

Figure 2.3: Four Common Distributions Shown as CDF and either PDF or Histogram

NORMAL

TRIANGULAR

LOGNORMAL

BINOMIAL

2.2 The Bare Bones of Probability and Statistics

2.2.1 Probability Density Functions and Cumulative Distribution Functions

Fortunately, both probability and statistics rely on pictures to illustrate ideas. Figure 2.3 shows four common probability distributions. Each one is shown in two types of graphs. In the top row are the probability density functions (PDF's). In the second row, we see the corresponding cumulative distribution functions (CDF's). In each case, the X-axis refers to some random variable, while the Y-axis refers to probability.

One more very common distribution is the uniform distribution, whose PDF and CDF will be introduced later.

Variables, Distributions, PDF's, CDF's, and More Language

What is a *random variable?* What is a *probability distribution*? For our purposes, a *random variable* is any variable that has a PDF or a CDF defined for it. Typically we use random variables to describe future events whose outcomes are uncertain. Random variables count or measure things that are of interest to us. We sometimes use the phrase probability *distribution* in connection with a random variable. It is acceptable to talk about a normally distributed random variable or a random variable having a normal probability distribution. Think of X as the random variable with two associated graphs, a PDF and a CDF. The distribution of X can refer to either of these graphs. These graphs tell us how the values of X are distributed. In Monte Carlo simulation, it is much more common to see a CDF than a PDF, for reasons that will be obvious later. When we construct a histogram from field data, however, we are approximating a PDF. The histogram of the sample may suggest a type of distribution, a shape of PDF.

Interpreting a probability density function may seem awkward at first, but soon becomes quite natural and will prove to be handy. The scale on the X-axis tells us the range of values of the variable. The height of the curve tells us how likely the values on the X-axis are to occur.

There are only two rules for PDF's.

1) The total area under the PDF is 1.00.

2) The area under the curve between X = a and X = b is the probability that X lies between a and b.

These PDF's are to random variables what histograms are to sampled data. The corresponding CDF for a given PDF is obtained by a cumulative process, just as CDF was defined for histograms.

There are only two rules that define a CDF.

1) The CDF curve ranges from 0.0 to 1.0 on the vertical scale and from the minimum to the maximum value of X. The curve is "monotonically non-decreasing" which is a fancy way of saying that the graph may have level segments, but can not go down.

2) The value on the y-axis corresponding to X=a is the probability that X is less than or equal to a (i.e., no larger than a).

CDF's make it easy to find the *median* value of X: wherever the curve crosses the 50-percentile line. About half the world draws their CDF's in **reverse** order from Figure 2.2, in terms of decreasing chance of occurrence. Figure 2.4 shows this orientation. The interpretation of the point (X=a, prob = b) is that the probability that X is **greater than** (rather than less than or equal to) a is b.

*Figure 2.4
Alternate
Style for
Cumulative
Distribution
Function*

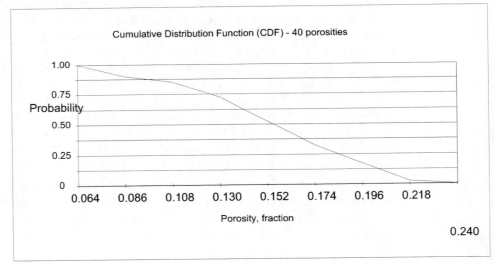

There is a simple mathematical relationship between the PDF and The CDF. If f(x) is the function describing the PDF curve, then the integral (i.e., the antiderivative) of f(x) is the function describing the CDF. In other words, the CDF is the area under the PDF curve. It is easy to see that a uniform distribution, which is the graph of the constant function Y = c, has an integral that is the graph of the function Y=cX + c' (a line). The relationship between other PDF's and their CDF's is not so obvious. You should be able to see, however, that the steep portions of any CDF correspond to the X-ranges with high probabilities in the PDF.

2.2 The Bare Bones of Probability and Statistics

Distributions - in the forms of histograms, PDF's, and CDF's - play an essential role in risk analysis. Many of the input variables in our models can be represented by distributions. Risk analysis is applicable when we have a degree of uncertainty about the values of some parameters in our models, whether it be area, net pay, recovery factor; number of dry holes we will drill before the first commercial discovery, the initial potential and the decline rate of a well we are about to drill, and so on. Distributions help us quantify these uncertainties. Moreover, when we complete a risk analysis procedure, the outputs are best described in terms of distributions. What is the range of NPV for this prospect? How like is it that the DCFROR exceeds 10%? How likely is it that we complete the project in 15 years? Questions like these beg for distributions. We need to familiarize ourselves with a variety of distributions so we can make good judgments about both the type of distribution to use and how to estimate the exact shape of the distribution of a given type.

2.2.2 Discrete vs Continuous Models: Counting vs Measuring

There are two types of distributions: one kind represents *discrete* random variables, the other represents *continuous* random variables. Although it oversimplifies, we can think of *discrete* variables as those that **count** and *continuous* variables as those that **measure**. A discrete variable can take on values like 0,1,2,3..., whereas a continuous variable can take on any value in some interval of real numbers, e.g., any number between 20.0 and 30.0. The 40 porosities in Table 2.1 represent a sample from a continuous distribution. Presumably porosity could be any value between 0.065 and 0.230 (6.5 % and 23 %), even though we may round it off to three decimal places.

Examples of discrete variables

- number of sand units intersecting a wellbore
- density of natural fractures (number of fractures per foot)
- number of wells needed to drain reservoir
- number of (whole) years until production begins
- number of commercial wells
- number of dry holes
- 0-1 variables (either/or)

Examples of continuous variables

- initial potential of an oil or gas producer
- initial decline rate of a producer
- the price of gas or oil
- the annual cost of maintaining a producer
- porosity, areal extent, net pay, water saturation

- reserves

- NPV, DCFROR

Thus if we count the number of heads that occur in two tosses of a fair coin, then there are only three distinct possibilities: 0,1, and 2. We could draw a histogram for this random variable with columns or rectangles **centered** at these three values. The height of the columns provides us with a way to compare the likelihood (another name for probability) of each possibility. By contrast, 40 measurements of porosity were **grouped** into evenly spaced *classes* then displayed in a histogram whose rectangles represent these classes.

Note that sometimes the vertical axes represents the frequency (i.e., the number of items in the sample falling into each class), while at other times, we *normalize* these frequencies by dividing each of them by the total sample size. The result is a relative frequency histogram, where the vertical scale now indicates an estimate for probability.

2.2.3 Median, Modes, and Means - Measures of Central Tendency

Any distribution or sample of data, whether discrete or continuous, can be described to some degree by stating some measure(s) of central tendency, and some measure(s) of dispersion.

Common measures of *central tendency* are the *mean, median, and mode*. All three are useful at times, and often it is informative to specify two or three of these measures. The definitions are straightforward for discrete variables and for samples like our 40 values of porosity. Suppose the variable X takes on values x_1, x_2, x_3, x_4, x_5 with frequencies (probabilities) p_1, p_2, p_3, p_4, p_5. The *mean (or arithmetic average)* is given by

$$\text{mean (X)} = \sum_{1}^{5} p_i * x_i \qquad \textbf{(2.1)}$$

In the case of *sampled* data, the mean is simply the sum of all sample values divided by the number of values in the sample. This is equivalent to assuming that all sample points have the same probability $(1/N)$ of occurring. For the 40 porosities, the mean is given by

$$\text{mean} = \frac{1}{40} \sum_{1}^{40} x_i = 0.151$$

The *median of X* is the value corresponding to 50% cumulative probability. For sampled data, the median can be found by rearranging the data from smallest to largest and selecting the middle value. By convention the arithmetic average of the two middle points is used for an even number of points.

The *mode* of X is the particular x_i for which p_i is the largest, the X-value where the histogram is highest. Thus could be ties for the mode, if two or more classes contain the same number of data. By convention, if no class contains two or more data, there is no mode.

Examples. Here are several sample data sets with their mean, mode, and medians listed. You should check the simple calculations to verify each measure.

Set	Data	Mean	Median	Mode
1	10, 20, 30, 40, 50	30	30	none
2	10, 20, 30, 40, 50, 50	33.3	35	50
3	1, 30, 100, 7, 3, 3, 3	21.0	3	3
4	1, 1, 2, 3, 3	2	2	tie: 1 and 3
5	2, 2, 40, 4000,	1011	21	2

The first and fourth sets are *symmetric*. Once we calculate the mean value, the points pair off to the right and left of that mean on a number line. In this case the mean and median are identical. In many applications, when we have a symmetric distribution, the mode also coincides with this common value, but it doesn't have to as is evident in the fourth data set. You should note that when data consist of values of similar magnitude, the three measures of central tendency are fairly close. In the fifth set, however, the three measures can represent very different things about the data. Beware of the trap of thinking that any of these measures is the typical value for the data.

For *continuous* variables the *mode* is simple: it is the X-value corresponding to the highest point on the probability density function. The *median* is easiest seen from the CDF: the X-value corresponding to the 50-percentile on the vertical axis. The mean is more complicated. The official definition uses an integral and is the analog of the sum:

$$\text{mean}(X) = \int xp(x)dx \tag{2.2}$$

where the integral is taken over the range of X.

Take a quick look at the four distributions in Figure 2.3. For the normal, triangular, and binomial, the mode, median, and mean are identical. While it is not obvious, the lognormal distribution has the property that mode < median < mean.

2.2.4 Range, Variance, and Standard Deviation - Measures of Dispersion

The simplest measure of dispersion is the *range* of a distribution, defined as the difference between its *minimum* and *maximum* values. Thus the *range* of the sample distribution of Hancock porosities is 0.230-0.065 =0.165.

Variance and *standard deviation* are used to measure and describe the spread of the data or the random variable. Are the values clustered together or spread out? Again, these concepts are simple to define for discrete variables. Suppose x_1, x_2, x_3, x_4, x_5 are the values of X with corresponding frequencies (probabilities) p_1, p_2, p_3, p_4, p_5. and suppose m is the mean. The *variance, s^2* ,and its square root, s, *the standard deviation*, of X are given by

$$\text{variance (X)} = s^2 = \sum_1^5 p_i * (x_i - m)^2 \tag{2.3}$$

For *continuous* distributions the *variance* is an integral taken over the range of X: here we use different notation, μ for mean and σ for standard deviation.

$$\text{variance (X)} = \sigma^2 = \int (x-\mu)^2 p(x)dx \tag{2.4}$$

The following tabulation illustrates how we calculate variance and standard deviation for the 40 porosities.

x	$(x-\mu)^2$
0.161	.0001
0.112	.001521
0.149	.000004
0.169	.000324
0.11	.001681
0.207	.003136
0.146	.000025
0.131	.0004
....	....
totals 6.04	0.06519

The mean m = 6.04/40 = 0.151. The variance s^2 = 0.06519/40 = 0.00163, and thus s = √.00163 = 0.04.

Note: Strictly speaking, the variance and standard deviation calculated from **sampled** data provides us with an **estimate** of the variance and standard deviation of its parent population. Although we will use the formulas above for our calculations, statisticians use a slightly different formula: they divide by (N-1) instead of N to get the variance. It can be shown that the formula with N-1 is a better estimate for the population variance. For practical purposes, the results are usually indistinguishable at least for larger samples. In fact, statisticians reserve the symbol σ for the population standard deviation and often use the symbol s for the sample standard deviation.

To complicate matters further, in Excel, there are two functions each for variance and standard deviation. For example, STDEV divides by N-1, but STDEVP divides by N. Moreover, when you ask for descriptive statistics on a sample, the formula uses (N-1).

Incidentally, Excel has an add-in Analysis Tool called Descriptive Statistics. If you specify the 40 porosity values, after clicking on this tool, you point to a blank portion of the sheet and get the following table.

Mean	0.1510
Standard Error	0.0065
Median	0.1538
Mode	#N/A
Standard Deviation	0.0409
Variance	0.0017
Kurtosis	-0.6363
Skewness	-0.2644
Range	0.1656
Minimum	0.0648
Maximum	0.2303
Sum	6.0394
Count	40

2.3 Common Probability Distributions

The quality of a Monte Carlo simulation depends on the two things. First, what are the underlying influential variables? Second, the input distributions must represent the parameters being modeled. Is net pay lognormally distributed or normally distributed or what? Selecting the right distribution is not easy. @RISK's integrated BestFit software can be used to fit a variety of common distributions to field data and it provides a goodness of fit measure for comparison among different distributions.

Now that we know a little about distributions in general, we take a closer look at the four common distribution types introduced earlier in this chapter (See back to Figure 2.3.)

2.3.1 The Normal Distribution

In theory, the normal distribution PDF actually extends infinitely far in each direction. As a practical matter, however, this normal distribution extends only from about 70 to about 130. The mean of this normal is 100 and its standard deviation is 10. In general, any normal distribution extends approximately three standard deviations in each direction from its mean.

You should be able to tell that the probability that X falls between 90 and 100 is much greater than the probability that X lies between 70 and 80. It is difficult to estimate exactly what those two probabilities are from the PDF. It is relatively easy, however, to estimate these probabilities from the CDF for the normal distribution (especially with a large graph with plenty of detail). The cumulative probability corresponding to 90 is approximately 16% and the probability corresponding to 100 is 50%. The difference, 34%, is the probability that X fall between 90 and 100. By contrast, the probability that X fall between 70 and 80 is approximately 2.1%.

Table 2.3 provides us with an easier method to estimate probabilities for the normal distribution. This table can be found in any statistics text or generated easily in a spreadsheet (Excel has a canned function, NORMSDIST). The table represents the CDF for the *standard normal curve*, whose mean is 0 and standard deviation is 1. The values are generally given only from z=0 to z=3.0. For any normally distributed variable, X, a value, x, can be "standardized" using the formula

$$z = (x-\mu)/\sigma \tag{2.5}$$

where μ is the mean of X and σ is the standard deviation of X. The values of z usually range from -3 to +3 as the values of X usually range from three standard deviations to the left of its mean to three standard deviations to the right of its mean. Again, by definition the mean of Z, and its standard deviation is 1. Moreover, like all normal distributions, Z is symmetric. The next example illustrates how to use the standardized normal variable to calculate probabilities of X.

**Table 2.3
CDF Values for Cumulative Standard Normal Probabilities**

z	P(Z<=z)		z	P(Z<=z)
0.0	0.50000		1.6	0.94520
0.1	0.53983		1.7	0.95543
0.4	0.65542		2.0	0.97725
0.5	0.69146		2.1	0.98214
0.6	0.72575		2.2	0.98610
0.7	0.75804		2.3	0.98928
0.8	0.78814		2.4	0.99180
0.9	0.81594		2.5	0.99379
1.0	0.84134		2.6	0.99534
1.1	0.86433		2.7	0.99653
1.2	0.88493		2.8	0.99740
1.3	0.90320		2.9	0.99800
1.4	0.91924		3.0	0.99865
1.5	0.93319			

Example 2.1 - Estimating Probabilities Using the Standard Normal Curve

Suppose you believe that porosities (for a particular producing formation) are normally distributed with a mean of 15% and a standard deviation of 3%. What percent of porosities would be greater than 21%? What percentage of these porosities would lie between 10% and 20%?

Solution:

1) First calculate the z-score

$z = (.21 - .15)/0.03 = 2.0$

Next, read the probability from Table 2.3

$P(Z \le 2.0) = 0.97725$

We conclude that less than 3% of the porosities would be greater than 21%

2) This calculation shows how to use the Z-score table to get the probability that Z falls into some specified interval. First, calculate two z-scores:

$z = (.10 - .15)/0.03 = -1.67$

$z = (.20 - .15)/0.03 = 1.67$

From Table 2.3, look up

$P(Z \leq 1.67) = 0.9525$

and **by symmetry** infer that

$P(Z \leq - 1.67) = (1 - 0.9525) = 0.0475$

We conclude that

$P(-1.67 \leq Z \leq 1.67) = 0.9525 - 0.0475 = 0.9050$

Thus about 90% of the porosities would be expected to fall into this interval of 10% to 20%.

Normal random variables often describe measurements that have some natural average value where values greater or less represent deviations from the mean. Heights, weights, average seasonal rainfall, test scores (including IQ tests), percent of defective manufactured products, and diameters of ball bearings are typical measurements represented by normal variables. Many variables are treated as approximately normal.

In the oil and gas industry, normal distributions might be appropriate for variables which themselves are sums of other variables, such as production or revenue estimates from fields found by summing over individual wells or grand totals of either costs or investments. Sometimes porosity, formation volume factors, decline rates, and saturations may appear to be relatively symmetric in shape and could be modeled by a normal distribution.

2.3.2 The Triangular Distributions

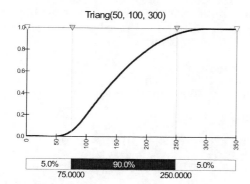

Figure 2.5a CDF for skewed triangular distribution.

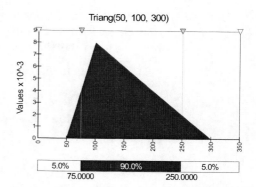

Figure 2.5b PDF for skewed triangular distribution.

The (symmetric) triangular distribution shown in Figure 2.3 shares some features with the normal. Both distributions are symmetric and both favor values near the mean. Both have mean = mode = median. The triangular distribution differs from the normal in that it assigns relatively more weight to the extreme values. In some sense, the triangular distribution is merely a simple description of a variable which is more likely to attain values near its mode than it is near the extremes. Numerous reservoir parameters have been modeled using triangular distributions, including gross and net pay, area, recovery efficiency, porosities and saturations, productivity, expenses, and prices.

Many engineers and geologists have favored a skewed triangular distribution, whose mode is different from the average of the maximum and minimum values. Figure 2.5 shows the PDF and CDF for such a triangular distribution. When estimating high and low values for a parameter, many people prefer to guess at 10-percentile and 90-percentile values along with a most likely value rather than the actual extremes, the 0 and 100-percentiles. The distribution TRI1090, described in Chapter 4, can be used to represent these cases. In spite of the popularity of the skewed triangular distribution, using it to approximate a lognormal distribution can be quite misleading. Especially for values toward the "tail" or the skewed part to the right, the triangular distribution assigns far more probability that the lognormal.

One reason for the popularity of triangular distributions is that some simple relationships allow calculation of certain probabilities. Suppose X is a random variable that we believe can be represented with a triangular distribution. X might symbolize gross pay, for example. The expression $P(X \leq x)$ means the probability that X is less than or equal to some particular value x in the range of X. Thus $P(X \leq 45)$ would represent the likelihood that gross pay does not exceed 45 ft.

From the PDF, using properties of similar triangles and the formula for the area of a triangle or from the CDF, which is a pair of joined parabolas, we can deduce the following formulas for probabilities.

1) For any value x **less** than the mode,

$$P(X \leq x) = (x\text{-min})^2 / ((\text{max-min})(\text{mode-min})) \qquad (2.6)$$

2) For any value x **greater** than the mode,

$$P(X \leq x) = 1 - (\text{max-x})^2 / ((\text{max-min})(\text{max-mode})) \qquad (2.7)$$

3) $$\text{mean} = (\text{min} + \text{mode} + \text{max})/3 \qquad (2.8)$$

Example 2.2 Estimating Probabilities Using a Skewed Triangular Distribution.

Suppose you believe that gross pay for a particular producing formation has a triangular distribution with a minimum of 40 ft, a mode of 80 ft, and a maximum value of 160 ft. What percent of gross pay values would be greater than 120 ft. What percentage of these porosities would lie between 60 and 120 ft?

Using the two formulas, we calculate

$$P(X \leq 60) = (60\text{-}40)/(160\text{-}40) = 0.17$$

$$P(X \leq 120) = 1-(160 - 120)^2/((160\text{-}40)(160\text{-}80)) = 0.83$$

We conclude that 83% of the gross pays would not exceed 120 ft and 66% (i.e., 83% - 17%) would fall between 60 and 120 ft.

2.3.3 The Uniform Distribution

Simplest of all, the *uniform* distribution is completely specified by giving its minimum and maximum values. Strictly speaking, there is no mode for the uniform distribution. As with all symmetric distributions, the median equals the mean. Calculating probabilities is straightforward:

$$P(X \leq a) = (a\text{-min})/(\text{max-min}) \qquad (2.9)$$

$$P(a < X \leq b) = (b\text{-a})/(\text{max-min}) \qquad (2.10)$$

Uniform distributions assign equal weights to ranges of equal width, whether at the extremes or near the mean. Thus the *uniform* is even more extreme than the triangular in this regard. Figure 2.6 compares the uniform distribution to both the triangular and the normal distributions in terms of the probabilities for intervals approaching the extreme upper limits of their ranges.

*Figure 2.6
Three
Common
PDF's,
Comparing
Probabilities
for Extreme
Ranges*

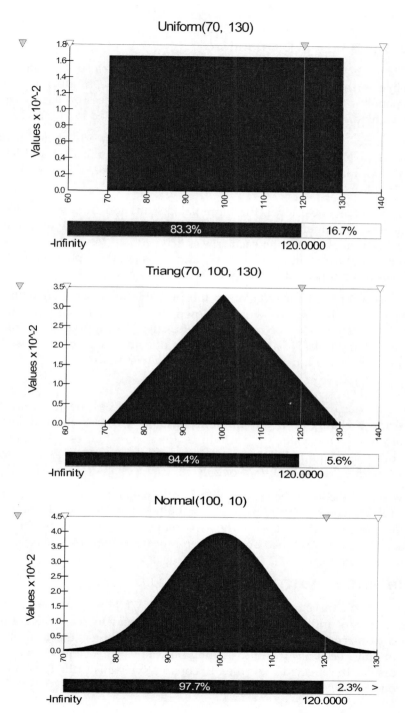

2.3.4 The Binomial Distribution

The *binomial* distribution is an example of a *discrete* distribution. A random variable X that is binomially distributed counts the number of successes in n independent trials where p is the probability of success on each trial. When p = 1/2 the binomial distribution is symmetric, as illustrated in Figure 2.3.

Flip a fair coin twice and let X count the number of heads. Possible outcomes are 0,1, and 2. Here n = 2 and p = 0.5 or 50%. Roll six fair dice and let X count the number of fours. The seven possible values of X are 0, 1, 2, 3, 4, 5, and 6. In this case, n = 6 and p = 1/6.

On a more practical level, the binomial distribution can be used to estimate the number of commercial wells you will drill in a 10-well program, where the probability of a success on each trial is, say, 20%. We would simply substitute C (commercial) for H and D (dry) for T and enumerate the possibilities. The random variable X would count the number of commercial wells.

There is a formula for calculating the probabilities associated with the binomial distribution. Before we write it down, however, we need to introduce some notation. Let us take the case of coin tossing. To say the coin is fair means that heads (H) and tails(T) have equal chances of coming up on any toss. Suppose you list the possible unique outcomes of tossing a coin twice:

HH, HT, TH, TT

The two outcomes, HT and TH, both represent one head - only the order of occurrence changes. If our random variable X counts the number of heads, it would assign the value "1" to both of these possibilities. Assuming these four outcomes are equally likely, we would conclude that P(X=1) = 2/4 or 50%, P(X=0) = 1/4 or 25%, and P(X=2)=1/4 or 25%.

Now toss the coin three times. With a little patience, we can enumerate the eight possible outcomes. Think of the possibilities associated with the first toss being heads (designated by H--). The two remaining tosses have the same possible outcomes as we described above. Then repeat the logic for the case where the first toss comes up tails.

HHH, HHT, HTH, HTT, THH, THT, TTH, TTT

Note that the three outcomes HHT, HTH, and THH all represent two heads. Thus P(X=2) = 3/8, and so on. The trick is to have a way to keep track of the number of ways to place two H's in three slots. As n gets larger, the task of listing all the possibilities becomes tedious. Listing out the various sequences of C's and D's in the case of 10 repeated trials (i.e., 10 consecutive wells drilled) would be extremely tedious. In fact, there are 1024 different possible sequences ($1024 = 2^{10}$).

Fortunately, there is a shortcut. The symbol C(n, x) refers to the *number of combinations of n things taken x at a time*. It represents the number of ways you can arrange x things in n slots. Thus C(2,1) = 2 (i.e., one H in two slots) and C(3,2) = 3 (i.e., two H's in three slots). The formula for C(n, x) involves the *factorial* function:

$$n! = 1(2)(3)(4)...(n) \tag{2.11}$$

where by definition, 0! = 1. Then we define

$$C(n, x) = n! / [x!(n-x)!] \tag{2.12}$$

A table of values of this function arranged so that n corresponds to rows and x to positions in each row shown in Table 2.4. It is called Pascal's Triangle

Table 2.4 Pascal's Triangle, Containing Binomial Coefficients

C(0,x) for x = 0	1
C(1,x) for x = 0,1	1 1
C(2,x) for x = 0,1,2	1 2 1
C(3,x) for x = 0,1,2,3	1 3 3 1
C(4,x) for x = 0,1,2,3,4	1 4 6 4 1
C(5,x) for x = 0,1,2,3,4,5	1 5 10 10 5 1
....	....

Here the pattern is easy to follow: each number is the sum of the two values immediately above it. A related fact is that each row represents the binomial coefficients used to expand the powers $(a+b)^n$ starting with n=0.

Let's get on with our formula for the binomial distribution. It is customary for discrete distributions to specify the probability of a particular value, x, of X rather than all values less than or equal to x. We let B(x, n, p) represent the probability that X = x for a binomial distribution with parameters n and p. Then

$$B(x, n, p) = C(n, x)p^x(1-p)^{(n-x)} \tag{2.13}$$

Figure 2. 7 illustrates the histogram (taking the place of the PDF) and the corresponding CDF for a binomial distribution with parameter values n=10 and p=0.5.

Note: Although we will not prove it, the *mean* and variance of **any** binomial distribution have simple formulas:

$$\text{mean of Binomial} = np \tag{2.14a}$$

$$\text{variance of Binomial} = np(1-p) \tag{2.14b}$$

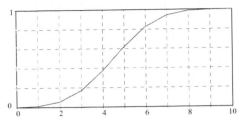

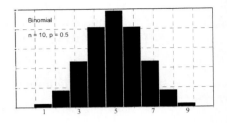

Figure 2.7 Binomial Histogram and CDF for n = 10, p = 0.5

Note: As illustrated in Figure 2.7, with a little care, any discrete variable can be represented by a histogram or a CDF, just like a continuous variable or grouped sample data. Each value K of the discrete variable is the center for a histogram column. The class boundaries (the base of the column) should extend from K-1/2 to K+1/2. To get the CDF, you first build the cumulative histogram and then connect the lower left-hand corner of each column to its upper right-hand corner. The resulting CDF can be used for Monte Carlo sampling as described in the next chapter, provided some provision is made for "gaps" in the original histogram, which correspond to extended flat sections of the cumulative histogram.

Example 2.3 Estimating probabilities using a binomial distribution

Your historic success rate for rank wildcats in the Williston basin has been 1/6. What is the probability that you will discover **at least 2** commercial wells in the next six wildcats you drill? What is the probability that you will have six dry holes?

Using equation 2.13, we find

$$B(0,6,1/6) = 0.3349$$
$$B(1,6,1/6) = 0.4019$$

We conclude that the chance of either 0 or 1 success is 0.3349+0.4019 = 74%, and so the chance of at least 2 commercial wells is 26% (= 1-(0.3349+0.4019)). The chance of all dry holes is 33%.

Example 2.4 Gambler's Ruin

A classic problem is to estimate the chance of going broke before you strike it rich. There are several interpretations of this problem. Let us say that you play a game where you have a 50% chance of winning or losing $1. For example, you bet your friend $1 that a single flip of a coin will come up heads. The coin is flipped and tails comes up. You repeat the game, but double your bet (double or nothing strategy). Now if tails comes up, you lose $2 for a cumulative total of $3. If you win, however, your cumulative total is ($2-$1) or $1. If you lose this second game, you double your bet again. Now losing results in a cumulative loss of $1 + $2 + $4 = $7, and winning results in a profit of $4 - $2 - $1 = $1.   Your reasoning is that **eventually** you will win the toss and come out $1 ahead. There is a fly in this ointment: the stakes keep rising rapidly. Seven consecutive losses would raise the stakes to 2^7 or \$128. You have to have "deep pockets" to keep playing. Quitting before you win, however, results in a sizable loss: the gambler's ruin.

This progressive-stakes makes the point dramatically, but on a more practical level gambler's ruin describes any venture where you may exhaust your available funds with a sequence of "failures" even though the expected value of the venture is favorable. If you plan to drill 10 wells where your estimated success rate is 50%, there is a chance that you will drill 10 consecutive dry holes. If you can't afford to have 10 consecutive dry holes, then you are a candidate for gambler's ruin.

From Table 2.4a we can see that the chance of 10 failures in 10 tries is 0.001, or 0.1% when p=1/2. When p=0.2, this unlucky streak of 10 has a 10% chance of happening. Although you could build a table for gambler's ruin by using the binomial tables, there is a special distribution called the *geometric* distribution (see section 4.2.2) which calculates the probability of x failures prior to the first success.

2.3.5 The Lognormal Distribution

The *lognormal* distribution is quite common in the oil and gas industry. It describes variables which are highly *skewed to the right*, which means that large values of X have much smaller probabilities than values of X in the opposite direction. As we shall see in detail in Chapter 4, lognormal distributions describe variables that are products of other variables. A case in point is reserves, N = AhR, where A, h, and R represent drainage area, net pay and recovery, respectively. We will see that N tends to have a lognormal shape. Parameters that are often thought to be lognormally distributed include drainage areas, gross and net pay, reserves, recovery, present value, absolute value of price changes, and values bid for leases. Outside the petroleum industry, incomes and various particle measurements (diameters, weights, volumes) are often lognormally distributed.

By definition, a random variable X has a lognormal distribution if ln(X) is normally distributed. Like the normal, the lognormal requires two parameters to specify a particular member of the lognormal family, the mean, μ and the standard deviation, σ. Also like the normal distribution, values for a lognormally distributed variable extend infinitely far in each direction. As a practical mater, many of the parameters that we model with lognormal distributions have finite ranges.

When the standard deviation is relatively small compared to the mean, a lognormal distribution resembles a normal distribution. For instance when $\mu = 100$ and $\sigma = 10$, you can barely see the difference between the two types of distributions. In field data for oil field reserves, however, it is common for μ and σ to be essentially the same size. Then there is a marked difference between the two distribution types.

When we suspect that a variable is lognormally distributed, and we have a sample of data, we should take the natural logs of the data and examine them for normal distribution tendencies (by plotting their histogram or CDF, or by more sophisticated statistical methods, which are beyond the scope of this book). The software package @RISK can be especially helpful in this regard.

2.4 Confidence Intervals and Probability Intervals

When we illustrate a random variable with its CDF, we identify a symmetric interval on the X-axis determined by the 5% and 95% probability values. Strictly speaking this is called a 90% probability interval, but is often referred to in the petroleum industry as a 90% confidence interval. [Confidence intervals are used in statistical hypothesis testing.] We use this range of X values to represent a very likely set of possible values that X could attain. That is we are reasonably confident that a randomly selected value of X would fall within this range.

Let us compare the 90% confidence intervals for three distributions, the normal, triangular, and uniform, each having a full range from 70 to 130. In the case of the normal, the 10 to 130 range represents three standard deviations from its mean of 100.

For the normal distribution in Figure 2.3, for example, the 90% confidence interval is from approximately **83.5 to 116.5**. We get these values from Table 2.3, our standard normal curve. The corresponding range for the triangular distribution from 70 to 130 is about **79.5 to 120.5**. The uniform distribution from 70 to 130 would have for its 90% confidence interval the range **73 to 127**.

2.5 Dependent Events, Conditional Probability, Value of Information

Much of this book deals with continuous distributions. Both the input and the output parameters of Monte Carlo simulation models for the oil and gas industry tend to be measurements rather than enumerations. The only discrete distribution studied so far, the binomial distribution, is popular because it helps describe success and failure in general terms.

On the other hand, Monte Carlo simulation is but one of many tools used in a broader framework of decision making. A decision tree is another popular tool, which also relies on probability and statistics. We digress momentarily to build on the binomial distribution discussion and relate it to decision tree analysis.

One of the assumptions of the binomial distribution is that the individual trials are independent of one another. If a fair coin comes up heads on the first toss, it still has a 50% chance of coming up heads on the second toss. In addition to coin tossing, dice rolling, and wheel spinning, there is a conceptual device useful to explain probability: drawing cards from a deck. There are two basic procedures: *drawing with and without replacement.*

Take a poker deck having 52 cards, four suits, 13 denominations A, 2, 3, ..., 10, J, Q, K. If you select a card, your chance of a Jack is 4/52. If you select a second card, your chance of a Jack is still 4/52 if you first replace the first card before making the second draw. If you do not replace the first card before the second drawing, however, your chance of a Jack is either be 4/51 or 3/51, depending on whether the first card was a Jack or not. When you draw *with replacement*, the consecutive trials are *independent*. When you draw *without replacement*, the probabilities assigned to the second draw *depend* on the outcome of the first draw.

For a second example to illustrate dependency, suppose you drill a wildcat well. If you drill another well offsetting the first, your estimate of success for the second well may be different from your estimate of success on the first well. You may have learned something from drilling the first well. Or you may have bought more or reexamined previous seismic data. Thus the probability of success on the second well may depend on the outcome of the first well.

There are times when it is appropriate to revise probability estimates based on additional information that has become available since the previous estimate was made. This section introduces conditional probability, Bayes' Theorem, and the value of additional information.

2.5.1 Conditional Probability

To say A and B are *independent events* implies that their probabilities are multiplicative. The chance of drawing a Jack is 4/52. The chance of drawing a Heart is 13/52. The chance of drawing a Heart which is also a Jack (i.e., the Jack of Hearts) is (4/52) x (13/52) = 1/52. Similarly the probability of tossing two Heads in succession is (1/2) x (1/2)=1/4. In symbols, if A and B are independent,

$$P(A \text{ and } B) = P(A)P(B) \qquad (2.15)$$

If we are told that the card drawn is a Jack, the odds that it is also a heart are unchanged.

By contrast, knowing that the drawn card is not a spade would alter the odds that it is a heart. The revised probability would be 13/39 (or 1/3) instead of 13/52 (or 1/4).

In many real life situations, it is more difficult to decide whether two events are independent. Take the case of drilling wells. Does knowing that well #1 was a dry hole have any bearing on the probability that Well #2 will be dry? IT DEPENDS ON THE SITUATION!

Let's suppose you decide to drill 10 wells in a new play type and the first well is dry. Company wisdom estimates that of 100 possible structures to drill on, 15 will prove to be commercial. Before you drilled the first well, you estimated the probability of success to be 15/100 or 15%. Suppose that logging and other data from the well was inconclusive. What are your odds for success in a second well?

Some people argue that the new odds should be 15/99. They argue that you have drawn without replacement. Others would argue that the odds remain unchanged: 15/100. Still others argue that the odds have decreased, because of geologic dependency between the two locations. Some interesting papers have been written on this and related subjects. Two of them included in our references, by Baker(1988) and Smith(1974) are definitely thought-provoking. We won't try to resolve this apparent dilemma here.

There is special notation used for probability of combined events. P(A and B) means the joint probability of A and B occurring. P(A|B) is the conditional probability of A knowing B occurred. When two events are mutually exclusive (can't both occur simultaneously) and exhaustive (when one or the other must occur), then the sum of their probabilities is 1.0. When a coin is tossed, either Heads or Tails occurs. When a die is rolled, either a "4" or "not a 4" comes up. Think of mutually exclusive and exhaustive events as the totality of possible outcomes separated into two distinct groups. Here are some facts

$$P(A \text{ and } B) = P(A|B)P(B) \qquad\qquad (2.16)$$

$$P(B) + P(\text{not } B) = 1.0 \qquad\qquad (2.17)$$

$$P(A) = P(A|B)P(B) + P(A| \text{ not } B)P(\text{not } B) \qquad\qquad (2.18)$$

The second equation assumes that either B or "not B" has to occur for A to occur. It follows that either (A and B) or (A and not B) must occur, and since these events are mutually exclusive, the probability of A is their sum.

Warning. We use language like "knowing B has occurred" and "once we know B" when we discuss conditional probability. The actual sequence of A and B in time is irrelevant as we shall see. In particular, we are often interested in both P(A|B) and P(B|A).

2.5.2 Bayes' Theorem

Refer to Figure 2.8, where there are more than two events B_1, B_2, ..., B_n which are mutually exclusive and exhaustive. We have generalizations of the formulas above.

Figure 2.8 Event A Preceded by One of Several Possible Events B_1, B_2, ..., B_n.

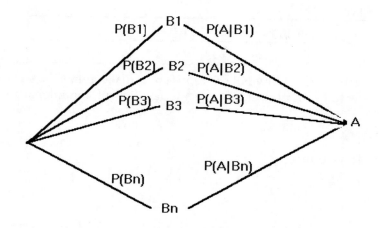

$$P(A \text{ and } B_j) = P(A \mid B_j)P(B_j) \qquad (2.19)$$

$$P(A) = P(A \mid B_1)P(B_1) + P(A \mid B_2)P(B_2) + ... + P(A \mid B_n)P(B_n) \qquad (2.20)$$

$$P(B_j \mid A) = [P(A \mid B_j)P(B_j)]/P(A) \qquad (2.21)$$

The first equation (2.19) replaces (2.16) when A and B are dependent. The second equation (2.20) generalizes (2.18). The third equation (2.21) is *Bayes'* Theorem. It can be used to revise estimates of probabilities based on additional information. It tells us how to revise the probability of B_j, once we know A occurred, namely by multiplying $P(B_j)$ by the ratio $P(A \mid B_j)/P(A)$. Until you become familiar with this fact, Bayes' Theorem may seem complicated. No proof is offered here for the theorem, though it is actually straightforward. Instead let us apply the technique.

Example 2.5 Estimating Conditional Probabilities Using Bayes' Theorem

You are facing a "drill" vs "don't drill" decision similar to the one outlined in Chapter 1 when decision trees were introduced. After reviewing the technical data, your boss wants you to consider hiring a consultant with extensive experience in prioritizing prospects. You gather the data in Table 2.5 about the accuracy of the consultant's predictions from his previous work. The table is read as follows. For all the dry holes that occurred, the consultant (had) predicted 90% of them would be dry, but 10% would be commercial.

Table 2.5

Consultant's Predictions: Knowing How the Well Turned Out, What Percent of the Predictions were Correct?

	How the well turned out	
Prediction:	Dry Hole	Commercial
"Dry Hole"	90%	30%
"Commercial"	10%	70%
Total	100%	100%

Let D represent (actual) dry hole, C represent actual commercial well with "D" and "C" representing the predictions. In the notation of conditional probability, the table says

$P(\text{"D"} | D) = 0.90$

$P(\text{"C"} | D) = 0.10$

$P(\text{"D"} | C) = 0.30$

$P(\text{"C"} | C) = 0.70$

You are interested in the accuracy of the prediction for **future** wells. You want to know how much credence to place on a prediction of a dry hole. That is, if the consultant predicts your well will be dry, what probability should you assign to a dry hole in your decision analysis? Think about it. The answer is not necessarily to assign 90% probability that the well will be dry. In conditional probability notation you want to estimate $P(D | \text{"D"})$ and so on.

Before calculating the necessary probabilities in this example, you need to have your own estimates for dry holes independent of the consultant's predictions. These are called prior or *a priori* estimates. A decision tree will summarize some information. For simplicity, we scale down the tree in Chapter 1 (Figure 1.7). We then add a branch with a third alternative: hire the consultant. The probabilities at the top branch are your company's best estimates for dry hole (40%) and commercial well (60%). We simplified the outcomes to simply "dry" hole and "commercial" (rather than indicate level of success). Refer to Figure 2.9 for the completed tree.

Figure 2.9
Tree
Diagram
with Branch
Included for
Additional
Information

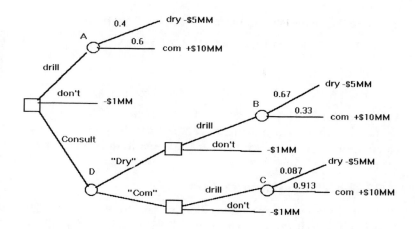

The first thing to do is calculate four conditional probabilities. These are the *revised* estimates of the two outcomes based on the consultant's predictions.

$$P(D|"D") = \frac{P("D"|D)P(D)}{P("D"|D)P(D) + P("D"|C)P(C)} = \frac{0.9*0.4}{0.9*0.4 + 0.3*0.6} = 0.67$$

$$P(C|"D") = \frac{P("D"|C)P(C)}{P("D"|D)P(D) + P("D"|C)P(C)} = \frac{0.3*0.6}{0.54} = 0.33$$

$$P(C|"C") = \frac{P("C"|C)P(C)}{P("C"|D)P(D) + P("C"|C)P(C)} = \frac{0.7*0.6}{0.1*0.4 + 0.7*0.6} = 0.913$$

$$P(D|"C") = \frac{P("C"|D)P(D)}{P("C"|D)P(D) + P("C"|C)P(C)} = \frac{0.1*0.4}{0.46} = 0.087$$

These values turn out to be

P(D | "D") = 0.36/0.54 = 0.67

P(C | "D") = 0.18/0.54 = 0.33

P(D | "C") = 0.04/0.46 = 0.087

P(C | "C") = 0.42/0.46 = 0.913

Examine the two distinct denominators:

$$P("D") = P("D"|D)P(D)+P("D"|C)P(C) = 0.54$$

and

$$P("C") = P("C"|D)P(D)+P("C"|C)P(C) = 0.46$$

What do these numbers mean? $P("C")$ is the percentage of dry hole predictions. Remember that we are using an "actual" dry hole percent of 40% ($= P(D)$) in these calculations. So we conclude that the consultant is likely to predict a dry hole 54% of the time.

2.5.3 The Value of Information

As a final step, you should recalculate the tree in Figure 2.9 with this new data. You will see that node B has an EV of $0MM and C has EV = $8.9MM. Thus, you would choose not to drill if the consultant predicted "Dry". Moreover,

$$EV(\text{Node A}) = (0.4)(-5) + (0.6)(10) = \$4MM$$

$$EV(\text{Node D}) = (.46)(8.9) = \$4.1MM$$

One conclusion you can draw from this analysis is that the *value of additional information* is about $0.1MM or $100,000. Information of the type offered by the consultant is called *imperfect*. You must assign probabilities to its accuracy. *Perfect* information. on the other hand, would lead you to a different strategy: Knowing the well would be a dry hole, you would cut your losses and not drill (cost = $1MM). Knowing the well would be commercial you would drill and generate a profit of $10MM.

There are excellent discussions of the value of information in Newendorp (1975) and Clemen (1989). In the oil and gas industry, additional information may be available but its value may be difficult to assess. Additional seismic data, logs, drillstem tests, cores, fluid samples, and lab analyses are all examples of additional information that might be obtained. The cost is relatively easy to estimate. The benefits are generally more nebulous.

2.6 Subjective Probability, Expert Opinion, and the Need for Historical Data

Capen's paper, "The Difficulty of Assessing Uncertainty" was first presented at the 1975 SPE Annual Technical Conference. He reported on an experiment he conducted while traveling as an SPE Distinguished Lecturer. At each lecture, Capen would ask the audience to provide best estimates and confidence intervals for answers to 10 questions. Sometimes he instructed the people to give a 98% confidence interval, but other times he asked for 90%, 80%, 50%, or even 30% confidence intervals. Here are three of the 10 questions.

"1." In what year was St. Augustine (now in Florida) established as a Spanish colony?

"4." How far is it from Los Angeles to New Orleans via major highways in miles?

"7." What is the area of Canada in square miles?

A person taking the test might guess 2500 miles as an answer to question 4. His 90% confidence interval might be 2000 to 3000 miles, meaning that there is only a 10 % chance that the actual mileage is either less than 2000 or greater than 3000 miles. Nobody was penalized for making an interval too large.

The results of these experiments were startling to many, especially to the test-takers. On average, 68% of the intervals provided failed to contain the correct answer. That is, on average, people scored 3.2 correct answers and 6.8 incorrect answers out of 10. Remember that "correct" merely means that the interval you guess contains the correct answer! In essence, the intervals were more like 30% confidence intervals. Moreover, there was essentially no difference between the 30%, 50%, 80%, 90% and 98% percent intervals. All intervals were equally likely to miss the correct answer.

Among Capen's conclusions were that people tend to be too proud of their estimates. One redeeming virtue did emerge. The more people know about a subject, the larger confidence interval they provide.

Similar experiments have been common in MBA classes. In one case, students were asked to estimate both the most likely and a 90% confidence interval for how many beans were in a jar. Although they were not allowed to use a ruler to measure the jar, they could stare at it and see the beans. In this experiment, 12 out of 33 test-takers estimated intervals that contained the correct number. It is interesting to note that three people used Monte Carlo simulation on the problem, estimating the dimensions of the jar (the inputs) and simulating the distribution for the volume (the output). These three estimated intervals were all correct.

Capen even offers some advice on what engineers and their colleagues can do to improve their estimating ability. One suggestion is to make up a 90% confidence interval and then treat it like a 30% confidence interval.

What is the moral to this story? Basically, one must be wary of estimates for ranges of uncertainty for the variables commonly used in engineering models. Even experts can be unreliable. What should we do?

There are three approaches to estimating parameters. We can be guided by historic data, fundamental principles, and expert opinion. If there is historic data available, it should be examined. Of course, to be usable in our models, historic data has to be appropriate. A plan to drill a horizontal well in the Austin Chalk, should not appeal to decline curve estimates from vertical wells in the Devonian Shale to estimate the production forecast. When an engineer builds an AFE for a rank wildcat in an emerging basin, she would not turn to cost estimates for infill injectors in the Permian Basin.

When historical data is appropriate and available, it should be used as our primary source to estimate the distributions – not just the range, but the shapes of the PDF or CDF. In Chapters 3 and 4, we will present some methods for incorporating historical data. Many of the tools outlined in this chapter will come to bear on that problem, as well as matters like dependency between parameters.

In some cases, at least the types or shapes of the distributions can be inferred from fundamental principles. There are good arguments why certain parameters should have a lognormal distribution: when they are products of other parameters, for instance. Similarly, some parameters represent sums of other parameters and would tend toward a normal shape distribution.

When no data is available and no fundamental principles apply, we may have to turn to experts. In that case, it might not hurt to ask them whether they have read Capen's paper.

Chapter 3: Designing the Monte Carlo Simulation Model

This chapter describes the steps necessary to design a Monte Carlo simulation. It begins with the sampling process - also called *Monte Carlo sampling*. This key step allows us to replace a number with a random variable. In effect, the statement

"The area is 400 ac"

is replaced with the statement

"The area is a triangular distribution with minimum value 200 ac, most likely value 400 ac, and maximum value 800 ac."

The replacement is not made a vacuum. Rather, we start with a specific model, such as the volumetric estimate of reserves, N, as a product of area, pay and recovery,

$$N = AhR \tag{3.1}$$

and we systematically replace each of the *input* parameters, A, h, and R, with probability distributions. Then we sample representative values from each of the inputs and calculate the result, N (the *output* of the model). That calculation is one of several hundred or even thousands of *trials* or *iterations* performed. The individual trials represent possible outcomes that are calculated before summarizing the entirety of the trials, using graphs such as histograms and CDF's as well as descriptive statistics such as mean, median, mode, range, standard deviation, and variance.

The whole procedure is a called *simulation*. The end result is to estimate N, not with a point estimate or a single number, but as a distribution. Once these simple mechanics become second nature, the user can address more subtle issues:

- Are the inputs independent?
- How should we arrive at suitable distributions for the inputs?
- How can we validate our results?
- How many iterations should be run?
- To what extent is the model sensitive to any of the inputs?

We will use a spreadsheet program to do the calculations, a tool accessible to virtually any technical person in the oil and gas industry. The very nature of Monte Carlo simulation demands some sort of computer. The additional features of graphs and database management makes Microsoft Excel the obvious choice for our applications.

Simulation software for mainframe computers has been available for decades, long before PC's were common. Still used today, but rapidly losing ground to the PC are simulation programs, both commercial and proprietary, written in FORTRAN, BASIC, PASCAL and C as well as in special languages such as LISP and GASP. The choice to restrict our attention to spreadsheet methods was based on a belief that most readers would find it a convenient means of designing and running simple simulation models.

3.1 Sampling from CDF's (Monte Carlo Sampling)

Monte Carlo sampling consists of obtaining a representative value of some random variable, i.e., of some designated probability distribution. The process can be viewed two step. First, select a *uniformly distributed* value between 0 and 1. Second, use the CDF for the distribution of interest to identify a value of its random variable. We can illustrate the process with some of the simple distributions introduced in Chapter 2. The first order of business, however, to generate uniformly distributed variables.

3.1.1 Generating Uniformly Distributed Values Between 0 and 1

Figure 3.1 shows the PDF and CDF for a uniform distribution on the interval [0,1]. Each time we sample from this distribution, we obtain a number like 0.2218 or 0.7184. Note that we have already imposed a convention that the number of digits is 4. How can we generate a sequence of such numbers? The answer has changed over the past few decades. Here are some methods people have used.

1) Using a roulette (type) wheel, with 10 numbers:

0,1,2,3,4,5,6,7,8,9.

We could spin the wheel four times and get 3,6,1,4. We could let these spins represent the number 0.3614.

2) Using a telephone book, we could choose the last four digits of a phone number selected at random. (Why not the first four digits?)

3) Using specialty books. We could visit a used book store and buy a book of random numbers. Books like this, along with trig tables, were common until calculators became popular in the 1970's.

4) Using a hand-held calculator, a random number can be obtained. Many calculators have a random number key.

5) Using a spreadsheet program, type =RAND( ) in Excel in any cell of the worksheet. Each time you recalculate the worksheet, you get a value of the random variable.

6) Using the spreadsheet add-in program, @RISK, which is designed to do Monte Carlo simulation, a variety of random number distributions can be sampled including the uniform distribution on [0,1].

Figure 3.1 PDF and CDF for Uniform Distribution on [0 ,1]

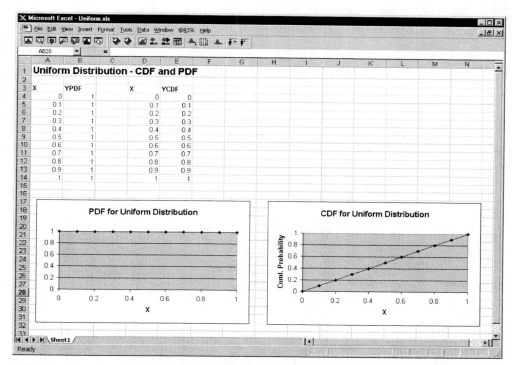

What does a sequence of random numbers drawn from the uniform distribution on [0,1] look like? How would these numbers compare to sequences drawn from triangular or normal distributions? The first column in Table 3.1 contains 20 numbers selected from the uniform distribution on [0,1]. We obtained them using @RISK. You could generate a similar sequence in Excel with the =RAND function. The other two columns in Table 3.1 contain 20 numbers each from triangular and normal distributions. The CDF's for these three distributions are shown in Figure 3.2.

Table 3.1
20 Values
Sampled
from each
of the
CDF's in
Figure 3.2

Uniform	Triangular	Normal
0.2553	0.3466	0.4011
0.9131	0.7939	0.7255
0.8900	0.7576	0.7013
0.3226	0.3978	0.4272
0.4375	0.4580	0.4639
0.5906	0.5517	0.5416
0.1667	0.2843	0.3535
0.0993	0.2179	0.2665
0.9351	0.8242	0.7630
0.4663	0.4645	0.4881
0.6907	0.6135	0.5503
0.1838	0.2934	0.3518
0.8989	0.7817	0.7222
0.7694	0.6490	0.6141
0.0276	0.1069	0.1856
0.2842	0.3691	0.4037
0.0453	0.1441	0.2229
0.6549	0.5871	0.5672
0.5891	0.5398	0.5454
0.8487	0.6955	0.6814

Figure 3.2a
CDF for a
Uniform
Distribution
on [0,1]

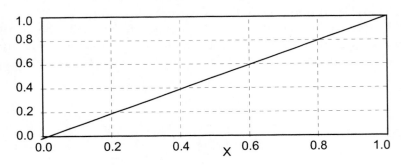

3.1 Sampling from CDF's (Monte Carlo Sampling)

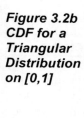

Figure 3.2b CDF for a Triangular Distribution on [0,1]

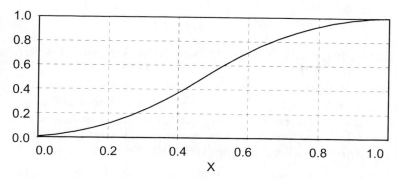

Figure 3.2c CDF for a Normal Distribution with Mean 0.5, Standard Deviation 0.167

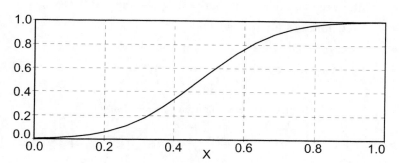

In the first column of Table 3.1, you might expect exactly 4 numbers (i.e., 1/5 of the total selected) between 0 and 0.19999999 (i.e., the first 1/5 of the range), 4 more between 2 and 3.9999999, and so on. That is what we would expect in the long run. For relatively small samples, however, we would expect approximately 4 numbers in each of the five equally spaced intervals.

Just how a computer program generates uniformly distributed random numbers in the interval [0,1] is of little importance to us. There are several formulas available, and random number generators have been around for decades, being one of the more common types of subroutines even in the early days of computers and calculators.

3.2 Sampling from any Distribution -- Graphical Approach

Now we turn to the matter of generating distributions other than the uniform distribution. Fortunately, there is a simple graphical interpretation. All we need is a CDF for the distribution of interest, coupled with a sampling procedure for the uniform distribution on [0,1]. The process is illustrated in Figure 3.3, with the normal distribution where we follow these simple steps.

- Start with a number from RAND uniformly distributed between 0 and 1,
- Enter the vertical axis at that point (We selected 0.2266),
- Move horizontally to the CDF,
- Move vertically down to the horizontal axis,
- Obtain a value of the desired random variable. We got 92.5.

Figure 3.3 Monte Carlo Sampling from a Normal CDF

Monte Carlo Sampling from a normal distribution

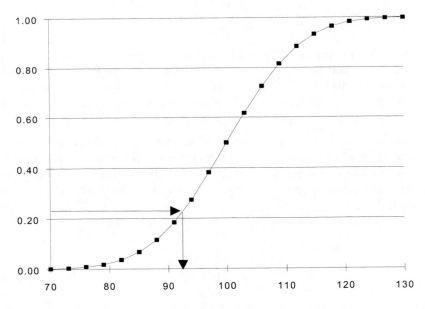

You should think of this process when you sample any random variable. Not only are we interested in common types of distributions like triangular and normal, but we want the capability to sample from our own distributions. When we have adequate historical data, we may not wish to appeal to any particular theoretical distribution. Instead, we use the procedure discussed in Chapter 2 for generating histograms and CDF's and sample directly from them.

3.3 Sampling in Microsoft Excel

Excel has several available distribution functions, listed in Table 3.2, in addition to the uniform. Spreadsheets of the future are likely to have even more built in distributions, although these canned functions are not designed for sampling and storing results, which can be tedious. Instead, we will rely on @RISK, which is designed especially for risk analysis, and has about 30 distinct distributions. We do not want a tedious method to generate random numbers, but we must understand the process.

Table 3.2 Partial List of Statistical Functions in Microsoft Excel

BETAINV( )	Inverse of the cumulative beta probability density function
BINOMDIST( )	Individual term binomial distribution
CHIINV( )	Inverse of the chi-squared (c2) distribution
EXPONDIST( )	Exponential distribution
FINV( )	Inverse of the F probability distribution
GAMMAINV( )	Inverse of the gamma cumulative distribution
HYPGEOMDIST( )	Hypergeometric distribution
LOGINV( )	Inverse of the lognormal distribution
NEGBINOMDIST( )	Negative binomial distribution
NORMINV( )	Inverse of the normal cumulative distribution
NORMSINV( )	Inverse of the standard normal cumulative distribution
POISSON( )	Poisson probability distribution
TINV( )	Inverse of the Student's t-distribution
WEIBULL( )	Weibull distribution

How to use these distribution functions for Monte Carlo simulation, depends on the type of distribution. The *discrete* functions, binomial, hypergeometric, negative binomial, and Poisson, can be used to generate histograms and CDF's which, in turn, can be used with VLOOKUP (a special spreadsheet table lookup function). Many of the continuous distributions are available in terms of their *inverse* function, as indicated by the names such as NORMINV() and LOGINV(). We list here only the inverse function when both are available. It is this inverse function which is used for simulations. If you simply want to generate PDF's and CDF's - as we did in Figures 3.1 and 3.2 - then you use functions like NORMDIST(), LOGDIST() and so on, which we omitted from Table 3.2.

The inverse function can be used directly to generate values of a random variable for simulation purposes. This is the precise counterpart to the graphical approach illustrated in Figure 3.3. After selecting a value from the uniformly distributed variable on [0,1], evaluate the inverse function at that number to sample from the desired distribution. The worksheet NORM.XLS, shown in Figure 3.4, illustrates the procedure. Cell B4 contains the formula =RAND(). Cell C4 contains =NORMINV(B$,1,0.33) which generates random values from the normal variable with mean 1.0 and standard deviation 0.33. The bar chart shown with the worksheet shows the result of 100 trials and approximates a histogram for the grouped data representing a normal distribution. The frequency table tells us that there were 2 points greater than or equal to 0 and less than 0.2, 20 points greater than or equal to 0.6 and less than 0.8, and so on.

Figure 3.4
Excel
Worksheet
that
Simulates a
Normal
Distribution

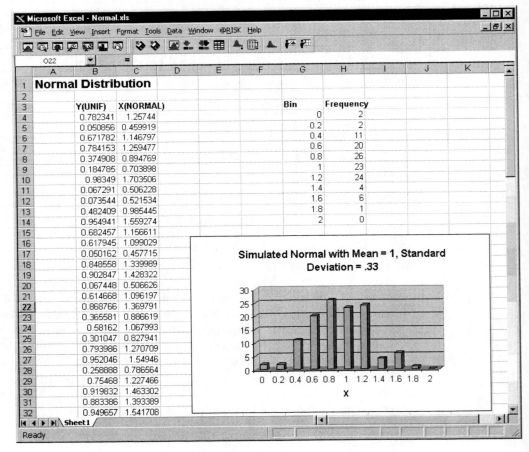

For the remaining distribution functions listed in Table 3.3, EXPONDIST( ) and WEIBULL( ), Excel simply generates PDF or CDF values associated with a specified input value of the random variable. The choice between PDF and CDF is made with a logical argument. Details of these functions are available in the Excel *Function Reference* Manual. To actually use these functions in a simulation you have to perform some spreadsheet chicanery. Moreover, the functions are fairly simple to program in any spreadsheet, so the special functions have little value.

3.4 Sampling Using @RISK

While you can perform simulations in a spreadsheet for several common distributions, including "homemade" distribution from historical data, the drawbacks are severe. Once you have the desired sample values, you still need to store the results and generate graphical and statistical analyses. Even the powerful graphics and statistical functionality of spreadsheets are cumbersome for complex simulations. For that reason, many users have turned to special Monte Carlo simulation software, such as @RISK from Palisade Corp.

As we shall see, @RISK allows the user to

- enter special distribution functions (*inputs*) in worksheet cells,

- identify cells as *outputs* whose values will be stored,

- specify a number of iterations,

- link cells with dependency relationships, and

- generate both statistical and graphical results from a simulation.

Since @RISK is a *add-in*, it runs inside of the spreadsheet, thereby affording the user the full functionality of the spreadsheet.

Rather than use 100 cells in a worksheet to generate 100 values of some random variable, @RISK requires only **a single cell**! That reason alone should be sufficient for anyone interested in running simulations in a worksheet. In fact, most simulations require several hundred iterations to achieve statistical significance. You can see this from the data we generated in the worksheets for discrete and normal distributions.

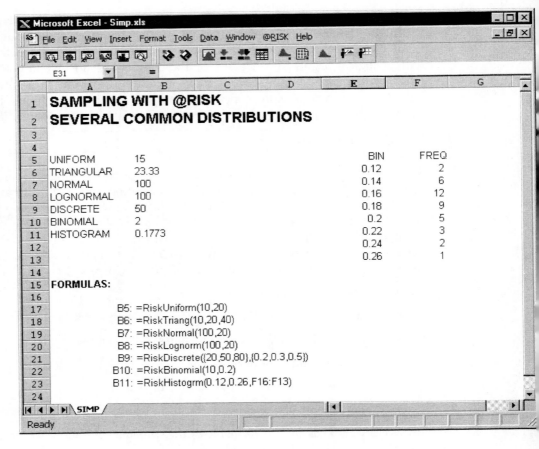

**Figure 3.5
Worksheet
that
Generates
Seven
Distributions
Using @RISK**

3.4.1 Example 3.1 - Sampling from Some Common Distributions

The worksheet SIMP.XLS, shown in Figure 3.5, contains input cells for seven distributions: uniform, binomial, triangular, discrete, normal, lognormal, and histogram. The @RISK formulas are listed with their cell references. Notice how each distribution requires only one cell in the worksheet. Of particular interest is the HISTOGRM function which references a range in the worksheet consisting of a frequency table. The histogram functions along with the companion function for any CDF, CUMUL, enable us to sample from any distribution, in particular historical data.

To run the simulation corresponding to Figure 3.5, we selected Cells B5 through B11 as output cells and assigned them the names in Cells A5 through A11. We specified 600 iterations and clicked the Start Simulation icon on the @RISK toolbar.

Start Simulation Icon

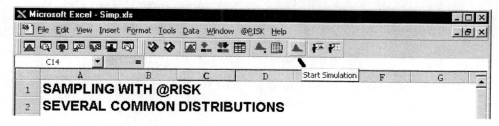

After the simulation, which took a few seconds, we switched to the @RISK Results window, where we viewed the histograms for each of our outputs. Then we copied the graphs and pasted them into our spreadsheet (after making a slight modification in the number of histogram classes).

Six of the histograms (we omitted the uniform distribution) are shown in Figure 3.6.

Figure 3.6 @RISK Graphs for Six Distributions after 600 Iterations

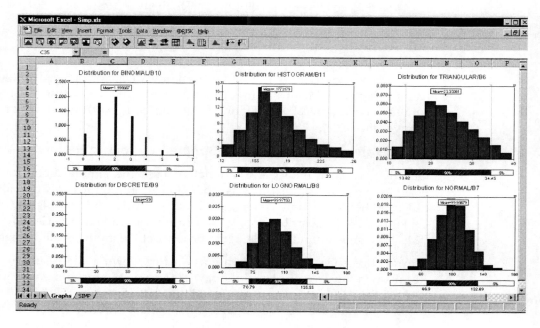

Chapter 3: Designing the Monte Carlo Simulation Model

3.4.2 Stratified Sampling to Achieve Your Goal More Quickly

Stratified sampling from a CDF divides the [0,1] interval on the Y-axis (the starting point for the process) into N subintervals (strata) and selects 1/N of the values from each of these strata. @RISK offers a stratified sampling method called Latin Hypercube sampling as an option. Its alternative, where random numbers are chosen for the Y-axis starting point, is referred to as Monte Carlo sampling. Thus we have two uses of the phrase Monte Carlo: the type of sampling and the overall simulation technique.

When we choose stratified sampling in @RISK, and specify 100 trials or iterations, the starting interval is divided into 100 nonoverlapping subintervals: 0 to 0.009999, 0.01 to 0.019999, 0.02 to 0.029999, and so on. In general, it is not necessary to have exactly as many starting intervals as the sample size, but that is what happens in @RISK. The idea is to obtain a representative sample from the population as quickly as possible - with as few trails as possible. This technique, although not without criticism, has been widely used in statistical research. From a practical point of view, using stratified sampling can reduce the necessary number of trials by a factor of about 1/3. What necessary means is that a further extension of the number of trials would not show an appreciable change in the results.

3.5 Running the Simulation

Now that we know how to sample from any CDF, we proceed to the next step: using sampled values from input variables to generate outputs. The process is summarized graphically in Figure 1.3 (Chapter 1), with our familiar volumetric reserves model.

3.5.1 Example to Simulate the Simple Volumetric Reserves Model

Our first actual Monte Carlo simulation uses the simple model of volumetric reserves, N=AhR. Simulating this model in @RISK requires only a small worksheet called AHR1.XLS, shown in Figure 3.7. The three input cells, B5, B6, and B7 contain TRIANG distributions, whose formulas are listed in Cells B12, B13, and B14. The single output cell, B8, is the product of the inputs, scaled down by 10^6.

We ran this sheet with 500 iterations. After viewing the results in the @RISK Results window, we displayed the raw data using the Insert menu Data command and returned to Excel, where we pasted the data into the worksheet. The results of the first 10 trials are included in Figure 3.7, suitably rounded off. While we were in the @RISK Results window, we graphed Figure 3.8, the distribution for N shown in both histogram and CDF formats.

In Chapter 4, we will discuss several variations of this model, including some from the petroleum literature. We will also discuss why the resulting distribution for N is skewed to the right. Another important feature of this simple model is that it ignores any possible dependency between the input parameters A, h, and R, an issue we will take up shortly.

Figure 3.7
Worksheet
that
Simulates
Volumetric
Reserves
Estimation

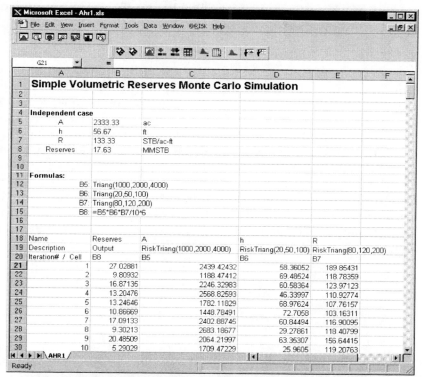

Figure 3.8
Histogram
for
Volumetric
Reserves
Estimates

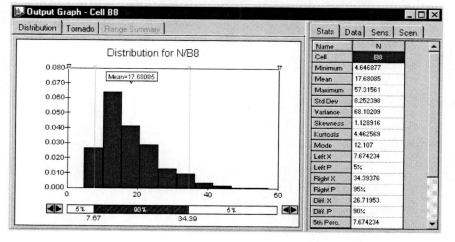

Example 3.5.2 A Stochastic Model of Exponential Decline.

For a second example of Monte Carlo simulation, we turn to the familiar production forecasting model for oil and gas wells, the exponential decline curve. The standard equation,

$$q = q_i e^{-at} \tag{3.3}$$

can be used with random variables for both q_i (the initial production rate, sometimes called IP) and a (the constant decline rate). Here the model has an additional parameter, t (time), which makes the output more complicated than the volumetric reserves output. No longer do we just want a distribution of numbers for output. Instead we want a distribution of forecasts or graphs. Our worksheet, shown in Figure 3.9 has two input cells, B4 and B5, and a column of formulas copied from Cell B10. The inset, which was generated in @RISK, shows the band of uncertainty associated with the forecast. The shaded region represents one standard deviation on each side of the mean. The dotted curves represent the 5- and 95 percentiles. Thus, between these dotted curves is a 90% confidence interval. We can think of the band as being made up of numerous decline curves, each of which resulted from choices of qi and a. Some possible decline curves might be

$$q = 135e^{-0.11t} \tag{3.4}$$

$$q = 275e^{-0.18t} \tag{3.5}$$

$$q = 196e^{-0.13t} \tag{3.6}$$

$$q = 71e^{-0.09t} \tag{3.7}$$

Plotting several of these curves would generate a graph similar to Figure 3.9

Figure 3.9
Worksheet
to Generate
Band of
Uncertainty
Around
Exponential
Decline
Curve
Forecast

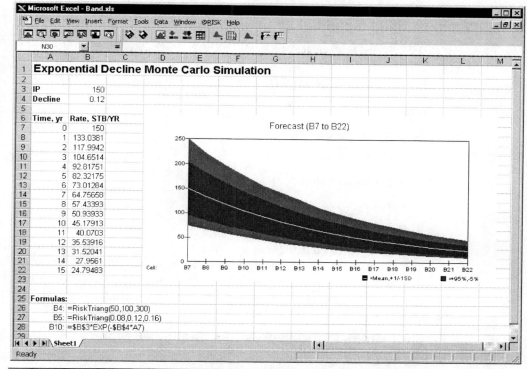

Figure 3.9
Worksheet
to Generate
Band of
Uncertainty
Around
Exponential
Decline
Curve
Forecast

3.6 Recognizing Dependence Among Input Parameters

One of the cardinal rules of Monte Carlo simulation is that the variables are assumed to be independent. In reality, many common models contain parameters that depend on each other. For instance, porosity and water saturation may depend on each other: in a hydrocarbon zone, rock with higher porosity often tends to have smaller water saturation. Other common pairs of dependent variables in volumetric reservoir modeling include permeability and porosity, and gross pay and drainage area. In production models, initial potential and decline rate or initial potential and gross (or net) pay may be pairs of dependent parameters.

Let us suppose we want to estimate reserves for an oil reservoir, using the expanded volumetric formula .

$$N = 7758 Ah\, \phi(1 - S_w) / B_o \qquad\qquad (3.8)$$

where

A = drainage area, ac

h = net pay thickness, ft

ϕ = porosity, fraction

S_w = water saturation, fraction

B_o = formation volume factor, BBL/STB

This is an expanded form of the simpler N = AhR model, but we ignore recovery efficiency, which was included in the R term. We will show how to capture dependency between porosity and water saturation and the effect it has on the product $(1- S_w)\phi$, which represents hydrocarbon porosity. Later we will extend the model to include dependency between area and net pay.

3.6.1 Cross Plots, Regression, and Correlation

Before we go any further, we need to discuss how dependency can be recognized and quantified. Suppose two variables, X and Y, are thought to be related to each other. The perceived relationship, known as *bivariate association*, can originate in at least three ways. *First*, there may be a cause-and-effect association linking the two variables: changes in the values of X lead to changes in the values of Y. Second, both X and Y may depend on a third variable, Z. Finally, there may be simply a "chance" association between X and Y.

The common device of plotting Y against X, a so-called "scatter plot" or "cross plot" may suggest some form of relationship; yet the exact origin of the association is not revealed from the graph.

Figure 3.10 shows a cross plot of two variables and the linear regression line generated in a spreadsheet.

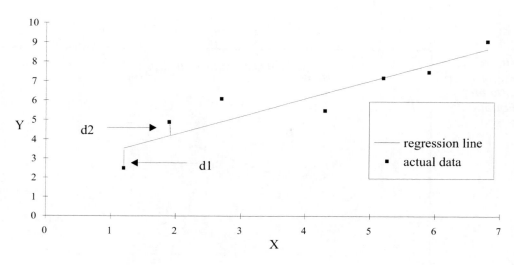

Figure 3.10 Cross Plot of Two Variables and the Linear Regression Line

The linear regression line is defined as the line that minimizes the sum of the squares of the vertical distances between the given points and the line. These distances – d_1, d_2, d_3, etc. in the Figure 3.10 – can be calculated easily. For a point (x_1, y_1), the distance is

$$d_1 = \left| y_1 - (mx_1 + b) \right| \tag{3.9}$$

The line is sometimes referred to as the "least squares line." While it is a simple calculus problem to find the equations for the unknown parameters, m (the slope) and b (the intercept), any spreadsheet program can do the calculation. Figure 3.11 was generated in Excel by highlighting the two columns headed X and Y in the worksheet Crossplot.xls, using the Chart Wizard to obtain the X-Y scatter plot, right-clicking on the points to add a Trendline with the option to display the equation.

Figure 3.11
Regression
Line and
Equation

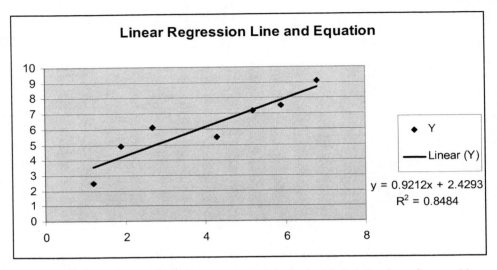

What does all this mean? The spreadsheet calculated these values for us. You should convince yourself that the slope and intercept match the line in Figure 3.10. The correlation coefficient is a measure of how the seven points cluster near the line. In general a correlation coefficient has a value between -1 and +1. A value r = -1 corresponds to a perfect negative correlation: the slope of the line is negative and all the data points lie on the regression line. Similarly a value r = +1 means perfect positive correlation, where the regression line has positive slope and contains all the data points. A correlation coefficient of 0 means that the points in question are not correlated. Their cross plot would be scattered; there would be no apparent linear trend.

Some data pairs are strongly dependent, but not in a linear fashion. Circles, quadratic curves, and exponential curves are made up of functionally dependent pairs. But if you did a regression analysis on such data, you would get correlation coefficients that vary from 0 to 1.

Whenever you have data pairs that you think may exhibit **linear** dependency, you need to find their correlation coefficient. In Excel, use the =CORREL function to get the correlation coefficient.

The correlation coefficient for n data pairs (x_1, y_1), (x_2, y_2),...,(x_n, y_n) is

$$r = \Sigma(x_i - m_x)(y_i - m_y)/(nS_xS_y)$$ (3.10)

Here x_i and y_i represent the data, m_x and m_y ,the respective means, and S_x and S_y are the respective standard deviations of the $\{x_i\}$ and $\{y_i\}$. You could easily calculate the correlation coefficient in a spreadsheet, but chances are that you would simply let the spreadsheet do it automatically for you.

3.6 Recognizing Dependence Among Input Parameters

Interpreting r requires caution. There is a sense in which r^2 represents the percent of variation in y associated with variance in x (as opposed to other factors). While the value of r = 0.9211 may seem like an indication of strong correlation, it is generally not wise to put too much faith in the number by itself. There are statistical tests to decide how significant the value of r happens to be. In general, if you have two sets of data having the same value of r, the one with the larger number of data points will have a "stronger" degree of correlation. Thus, if we had another set of data with 20 points and a correlation coefficient of 0.9211, it would be more strongly correlated than the data in Figure 3.10. We will see some examples shortly.

In some petroleum engineering situations, r-values might range as high as 0.50 to 0.75 (which we might describe as "moderate to strong correlation") The sign could be positive – as in area vs net pay or negative – as in porosity vs water saturation.

3.6.2 Example: Evidence from Offsetting Field

Suppose we want to simulate porosity and water saturation for a reservoir about to be developed. We have available data from another reservoir we believe to be similar. A cross plot of log-derived data from the analogous reservoir, shown in Figure 3.12, indicates that water saturation (Sw) and porosity (Phi) are inversely or negatively related to each other. That is, many completion intervals with larger estimates of porosity appear to have smaller estimates of water saturation. We want to incorporate an appropriate relationship between these two variables in our simulation.

Figure. 3.12 Cross Plot of Water Saturation Against Porosity

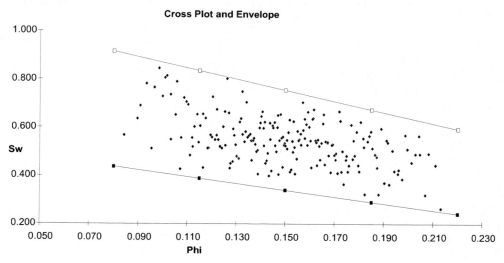

3.7 Incorporating Dependency in Simulation Models

There are several ways to handle bivariate correlations in Monte Carlo simulations. Two methods will be discussed, one that helps explain the relationship graphically and another that utilizes spreadsheet add-in functions. In both cases, Phi serves as the independent variable and Sw serves as the dependent variable. In the simulations, the independent variable is sampled first. Its value then influences the value of the dependent variable by restricting its range somehow.

3.7.1 The Bounding Envelope Method

The *bounding envelope method* (sometimes called the *box method*) begins with the cross-plot of one variable against the other and constructs two lines that represent the extreme values of data. These lines are shown with the actual data in Figure 3.12. The worksheet shown in Figure 3.13 can be used to run a simulation and then generate a cross plot of Sw vs Phi along with two bounding lines. One line bounds the data from below and the other from above. The two lines form an "envelope," which contains the data. If we add the vertical segments at each end, we have a "box" to contain the data. Note the *negative* slopes, indicating an *inverse* relationship between the two variables, i.e., the correlation coefficient, $r < 0$. To sample both variables, we first select a random value for the independent variable, Phi, and use it to determine the minimum and maximum values of the corresponding range allowed for Sw. Then we select a random value of Sw in this range.

The box method is not rigorous, but it has enjoyed popularity. One alternative for field data is to use multiple regression analysis. Another alternative, recommended here, is to use the rank correlation procedure available in @RISK as described in the following section.

Figure 3.13
Worksheet
for
Simulation
Using the
Box Method
and
Generating
a Cross
Plot of Sw
vs Phi
along with
Two
Bounding
Lines

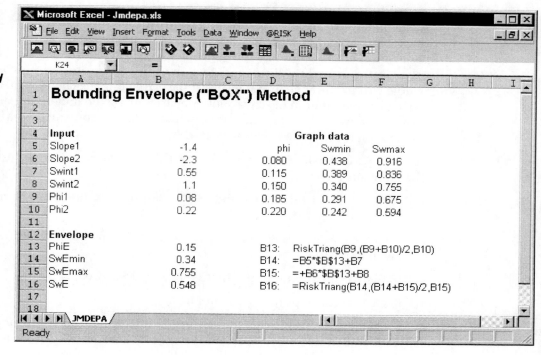

Figure 3.14 shows the steps used to sample a pair of variables using the box method. We enter the graph with our random sample of Phi, (approximately 0.170). We move up to each line and then off the vertical axis where we get a minimum value (approximately 0.300) and a maximum value (approximately 0.700) for Sw. Finally, we draw a random value for Sw from this restricted range of 0.300 to 0.700.

*Figure 3.14
Selecting
Two
Correlated
Variables
with the
Box Method*

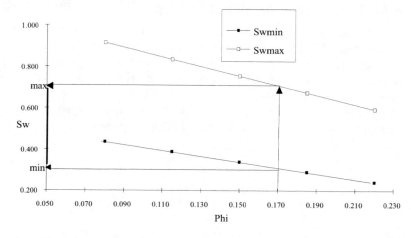

As mentioned, the choices of the particular distributions used for the variables is a separate issue. For instance, we could use triangular distributions for both variables. This assumes that the Sw values are clustered more toward a trend line between the bounding lines, and that the Phi values are more dense near the middle of the Phi-range than they are at the extremes. The choice is made based on the pattern of scatter in the cross plot or by examining the underlying distributions. Ideally, we would incorporate this actual data by constructing a cumulative distribution function for each parameter.

Let's take a closer look at the worksheet JMDEPA.XLS, as shown in Figure 3.13. The inputs include

- limiting values (minimum and maximum) for the independent variable, Phi, in Cells B8 and B9

- slopes (Cells B5 and B6) and intercepts (Cells B7 and B8) for the lines that relate Sw to Phi

- triangular distributions for Phi (Cell B13) and Sw (Cell B16)

- linear relationships (Cells B24 and B15)

Once a value of Phi is selected, the corresponding values (minimum and maximum for that iteration) of Sw are calculated on the two lines. Finally, we select a value of Sw from some distribution. If you have @RISK handy, you can use any distribution you like. If you are just using Excel, you can use the =RAND() function to generate *uniform* distributions for both Phi and Sw. The worksheet also contains a little table to generate a graph of the bounding lines (the envelope). Because the cross plot shown in Figure 3.12 was generated with triangular distributions, you should see more clustering toward the central region of both variables.

3.7.2 The Correlation Method Using RISKDEPC and RISKINDEPC

@RISK has the capacity to correlate two (or more) variables, without using the envelopes. We design a second worksheet, JMDEPB.XLS, for comparison (See Figure 3.15). Again, we designate Phi as the independent variable and Sw as dependent. We decide the extent of the dependency, which we quantify by a coefficient that can range from -1 to +1. Because we believe the two variables in question have a fairly strong inverse or negative relationship, we begin by choosing a value of -0.6 for the correlating coefficient.

Figure 3.15
Worksheet to
Simulate
Triangular
and Uniform,
Dependent
and
Independent
Inputs using
@RISK
Functions
DEPC and
INDEPC

Figure 3.15 Worksheet to Simulate Triangular and Uniform, Dependent and Independent Inputs using @RISK Functions DEPC and INDEPC

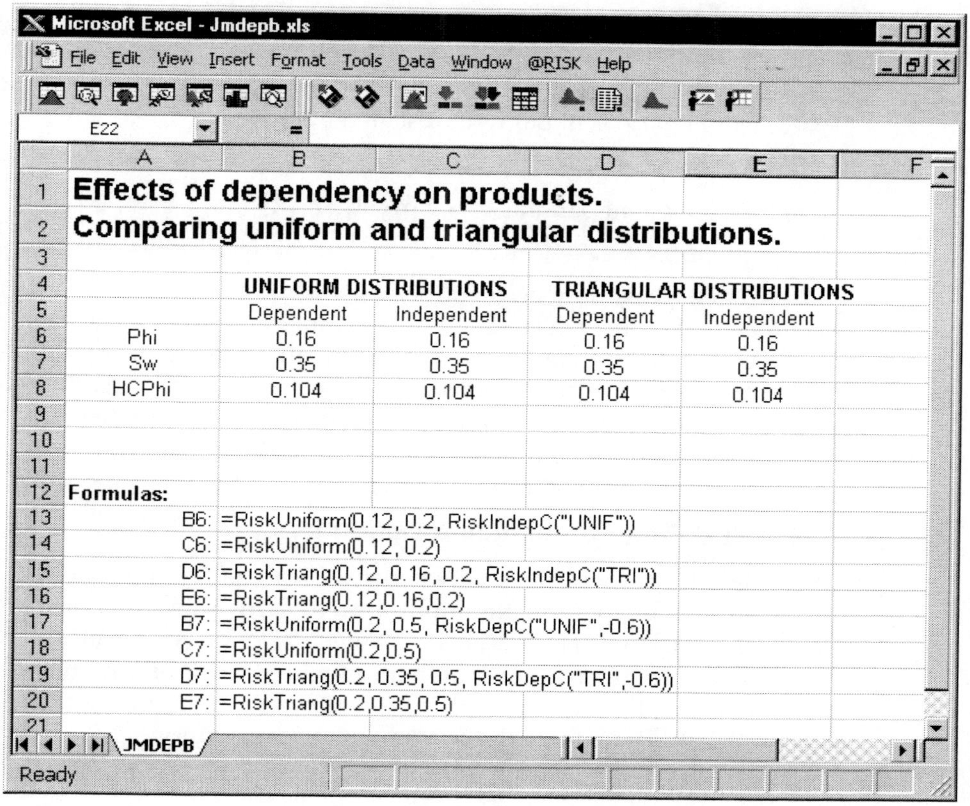

3.7.3 Rank Order Correlation

The distribution functions, DEPC and INDEPC, are based on the Spearman rank order correlation coefficient. The rank order correlation between two variables is simply the ordinary correlation coefficient when the **ranks** are used in place of the raw data That is, if there were 45 porosity values ranging from .103 to .224, then the value .103 would be replaced with the number 1 and the number .224 would be assigned the number 45. Once the ranks were assigned to each variable, the correlation coefficient, called the Spearman correlation coefficient, is calculated.

When the user indicates a correlation between two parameters, @RISK does some preliminary calculations before the simulations begin. First, it generates 300 values (or as many as will be needed in the simulation) of each random variable. These values are paired up in such a way that the resulting rankings would give rise to the designated Spearman coefficient. During simulation, when the independent variable is sampled (from among these predetermined 300 values), the matched value of the dependent variable is automatically used in the same iteration.

The two variables are linked together in the worksheet as follows: the independent parameter, Phi (in Cell B6) is represented by

```
RISKUNIFORM(0.12,0.20, RISKINDEPC("UNIF"))
```

and the dependent parameter, Sw in cell B7 is

```
RISKUNIFORM(0.20.,0.50, RISKDEPC("UNIF",-0.6))
```

Here "UNIF" is simply an identifier for this pair of variables. You might want to have several pairs of related variables in the same worksheet, each pair having its unique identifier . In fact, our worksheet features two pairs of linked variables, one using triangular distributions and the other uniform distributions. The distributions functions in both the dependent and independent variables can be anything – uniform, normal, triangular, etc. The value, -0.6, is the correlating coefficient (any number from -1 to +1).

3.7.4 The Effect of Including Dependency

For comparison, we can run two parallel cases. In one case, we use triangular distributions for both of the input variables, Sw and Phi. In the other case, we switch to uniform distributions. As a general rule, using uniform distributions for input variables leads to outputs with a wider range of variability – that is, more dispersion and hence more risk. The formula table included in the worksheet shows what is typed into the cells involving distributions.

Note that we include cells for hydrocarbon porosity HCPhi (= Phi (1-Sw)) as well as oil in place, N, which multiplies HCPhi by other factors that may be random variables. We concentrate on the values of HCPhi, because it is easy to see how directly that value is influenced by the choices in the four columns, whether to include dependency and whether to use uniform or triangular distributions.

Note that if we include dependency between Phi and Sw, then small values of Phi match up with small values of (1-Sw), and large values of Phi match up with large values of (1-Sw). The result is to make it more likely to get extreme values of HCPhi than would be the case if we treated Phi and Sw as independent variables. This same trend carries over to our estimate for oil-in-place N. We may get approximately the same range of possibilities, but the likelihood of being outside a given interval surrounding the mean is far less when dependency is ignored. In short, the output has a smaller variance when the variables are treated as independent.

Similarly, when we use uniform distributions for the input variables, there is a larger variance in the estimate for HCPhi and N than there would be had we used triangular distribution for our inputs.

As a practical matter, then, incorporating dependency between Phi and Sw leads to reserve estimates with greater variance. One interpretation of the risk of a prospective investment is the standard deviation (or sometimes the variance) of the expected present value. In turn, present value would be roughly proportional to reserves. Thus, if we ignore the dependency, then we underestimate the risk!

Does this mean that we should always use dependency and triangular distributions to reduce our risk? Absolutely not. Dependency between variables may or may not be present. It is helpful to look at data for those variables in similar prospects. The only reason to choose triangular distributions over uniform distributions is if you have historic evidence to back it up. In short, you need to analyze your historic data when it is available. See Holtz (1993) and Murtha (1993) for examples of dependence among oil reservoir parameters. In the absence of historic data, you need to rely on expert opinion, analogy, and underlying physical principles.

To see how the simulation bears out these predictions, we ran a simulation with 300 iterations. There were four pairs of data for porosity and water saturation, using *uniform* input distributions with and without dependency and *triangular* distributions with and without dependency. The four resulting cross plots are shown in Figure 3.16. Note how the triangular distributions cause points to cluster toward the center of the graph, whether or not the two variables are dependent. Note also how the dependency causes the data to exhibit a general downward trend, which appears to be more obvious with triangular distributions. If we were to change the correlation coefficient from -0.6 to -0.8 or -0.9, corresponding to r-squared values of 0.64 or 0.81, the clustering along the regression line would be much more pronounced.

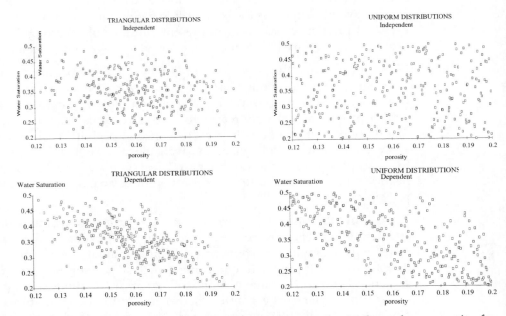

**Figure 3.16
Cross Plots
for
Combinations
of
Dependence
and
Distribution
Type**

We then generated the cumulative distribution curves for hydrocarbon porosity for each of the four possibilities, shown in Figure 3.17. The top graph shows the two cases that used triangular input distributions for both Phi and Sw. The bottom graph shows the two cases that used uniform input distributions for both Phi and Sw. In each graph, the steeper curve, resulting from independent variables, represents less risk: smaller variance from the mean.

Just how does this difference between independent and dependent pairs translate to our ultimate estimate of reserves? Remember that the Monte Carlo simulation doesn't just give us a number for reserves. The answer is a range of possibilities, with probabilities assigned to any particular subrange. The cumulative distribution curves for hydrocarbon porosity tell us that our estimated ranges would differ at both the 10% and 90% probability levels by approximately 5% in the triangular distribution inputs and 10% for the uniform distribution inputs. Thus, using independent estimates for porosity and water saturation could result in estimates whose range would be underestimated by 10% for triangular and 20% for uniform distribution inputs.

3.7 Incorporating Dependency in Simulation Models

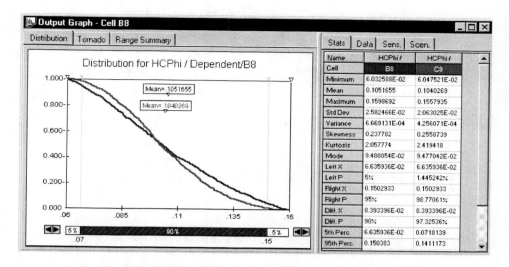

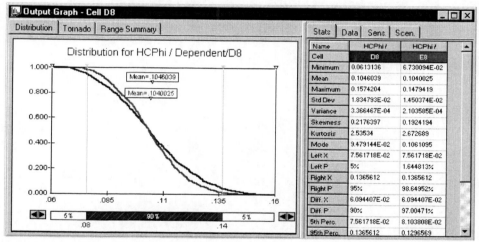

The steeper curve in each figure results from independent variables.

Chapter 4: Using @RISK - Applications for the Petroleum Industry

Having reviewed the necessary probability and statistics along with the basics of Monte Carlo simulation, it is time to put that knowledge to use. This chapter examines several problems that lend themselves to Monte Carlo simulation.

From here on, you should expect to spend most of the time at your keyboard, building and running models in Microsoft Excel. At the end of this brief introduction, Section 4.1 is devoted to the @RISK menus that appear when used with Excel. Section 4.2 describes all the majority of the distribution functions provided by @RISK. Sections 4.3 through 4.6 represent applications. Each application involves a worksheet.

4.1 Basics of @RISK Using Excel

The main objective of this section is to acquaint you with the @RISK menus and to step through a simple simulation. We will discuss entering distribution functions, selecting output cells, altering settings, running the simulation, viewing the results, and saving data, graphs, and statistics. We will not cover all the fine points of the menus. For instance, we pay short shrift to printing, sizing and enhancing default graphs, correlation matrices, distribution summary graphs, and running multiple simulations. When you finish this section, you should be able to design a simple Monte Carlo model, execute the simulation, and view the results.

For details on how to install or set up @RISK, please refer to the @RISK User's Guide. In addition, and perhaps most helpful in the long run, is the on-line @RISK help facility, accessible by pressing the <F1> key.

This book is accompanied by a disk containing worksheet files in Excel format. All the examples mentioned in the book are on that disk. To acquaint the new user with @RISK, we refer back to two worksheets from Chapter 3. The first worksheet, SIMP.XLS, is used to examine some of the common distribution functions included in @RISK. This worksheet is used to explore the @RISK menu. The second worksheet, AHR1.XLS, is built around a simple volumetric reserves model and features three input distribution function parameters and an output distribution of reserves.

4.1.1 Comparing @RISK for Excel and @RISK for 1-2-3

Although this book discusses @RISK for Excel, versions of @RISK are available for Lotus 1-2-3. Virtually all versions share the same assortment of distribution functions are available for input cells. Output cells and ranges of cells are selected and their contents are stored during the simulation. Results can be presented in the form of statistics, graphs (both histograms and CDF's), and raw data (the values in the output cells). The user has great flexibility in generating reports in both versions.

All that is necessary to run a simulation with any worksheet is to have at least one output cell selected and to have at least one distribution function in the worksheet. The fine tuning consists of changing the settings: number of iterations, type of sampling, specifics of reports, type of graphs and statistics, and so on.

4.1.2 Quick Tour of a Simulation with SIMP.XLS

Section 4.1.3 reviews numerous menu items that are not essential for bare bones simulation. If you want a whirlwind tour to start with, here are the steps. If you want a more pedestrian approach, go to section 4.1.3.

➢ Load Excel and @RISK by clicking the @RISK icon in the Windows Start Programs Palisade DecisionTools group or by opening the RISK.XLA macro after Excel is loaded.

➢ Open the file SIMP.XLS or reproduce it after opening a new worksheet (See Figure 3.5).

➢ Select the range B5:B11 and click the @RISK **Add Outputs** icon (the one with the single red arrow). Alternatively, from the @RISK menu, choose the **Model Add Outputs command**. A dialog box will appear. Enter the *Distributions* to name this range of outputs.

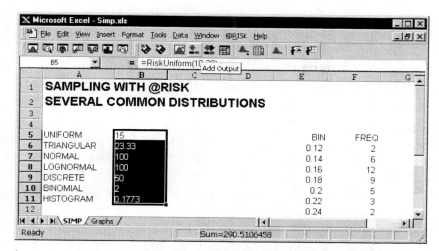

> ➤ Click the **Start Simulation** icon on the @RISK toolbar (the third from the right), or, alternatively, select the @RISK menu **Simulation Start command**.

> ➤ Watch the iteration tally in the lower left screen.

> ➤ In the @RISK Results window, hold down the <Ctrl> key and select the names of all outputs in the Explorer list on the left side of the window, right-click and select **Histogram** to generate all seven histograms.

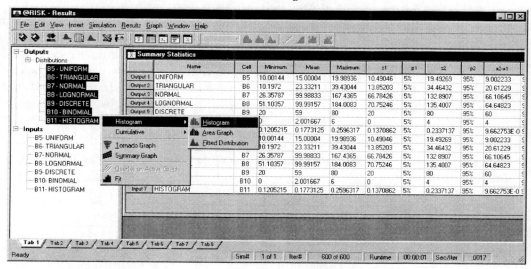

> ➤ Save the worksheet (Excel menu: File Save or Save as) and save the simulation from @RISK Save.

> ➤ Close the worksheet (Excel menu: File Close).

Congratulations! You just did a simulation.

4.1.3 Enter Probability Distributions

This section offers a leisurely tour through a simulation, pausing frequently to discuss menu items. The previous section provides the express version of the tour with no discussion of menus. Specific instructions are identified with an ➤.

After loading a worksheet or designing one from scratch, we identify those cells where we wish to replace deterministic values with probability distributions. Then we enter the appropriate distribution functions in those cells. What we see in those cells are the expected value of the distribution (See Excel Recalc below).

➤ Begin by clicking the @RISK icon in the Windows Start Programs Palisade DecisionTools group.

Excel is loaded along with the macro for @RISK containing libraries, distribution functions and the simulation software. We will be reproducing SIMP.XLS, and you should refer to Figure 3.5 while working on this example.

➤ Start with a fresh worksheet and enter the distribution functions shown in Table 4.1.1 into Cells B5..B11. To the left, in Cells A5..A11, enter the code names as shown: Uniform, Triang, etc.

The table shows the values that show up in the B-Column if the input is done correctly. These values represent the expected values of the distributions entered. In the cases of the two discrete distributions in the list, RiskHistogrm and RiskBinomial, the actual expected value is rounded off to the nearest value allowable in the distribution. For instance, the only values allowed for the binomial distribution are integers $0,1,2,..,10$. The actual expected value is $n*p$ or $10 *(0.2) = 2$, which happens to be one of the possible values of the discrete variable. To see how rounding occurs in the binomial distribution, try editing this cell, and type 0.15, in place of 0.2 for the value of p. The True expected value is 1.5, but the cell continues to display 2. Although more work, you could check to see what the true expected value of the RiskDiscrete variable happens to be. It is not 50.

Table 4.1 Distribution Functions and Cell Values in Worksheet SIMP.XLS

Distribution function typed into Column B	Value shown in Column B
=RiskUniform(10,20)	15
=RiskTriang(10,20,40)	23.33
=RiskNormal(100,20)	100
=RiskLognorm(100,20)	100
=RiskDiscrete({20,50,80},{0.2,0.3,0.5})	50
=RiskBinomial(10,0.2)	2
=RiskHistogrm(0.12,0.26,{2,6,12,9,5,3,2,1}) or =RiskHistogrm(0.12,0.26,F6:F13)	0.1773

The =RiskHistogrm function refers to a range of values in the sheet consisting of relative frequencies for equally spaced classes over the interval from 0.12 to 0.26. Until you type in values in the range F6..F13, the function will return ERR.

@RISK also allows you to define your distribution functions graphically. Instead of typing the distribution function directly in a cell you can click the **Define Distribution** icon on the **@RISK toolbar** and display a graph of the distribution you wish to enter. The @RISK toolbar is the second toolbar in the second row displayed in the figure here. The Define Distribution icon is the third icon from the left on this toolbar. The figure here displays the triangular distribution for B6. By changing the function listed in **Dist.** and the values defining the function you can change the graph displayed. Click **Apply** to add the function to the cell in your worksheet.

Defining a
Distribution
Graphically
in @RISK

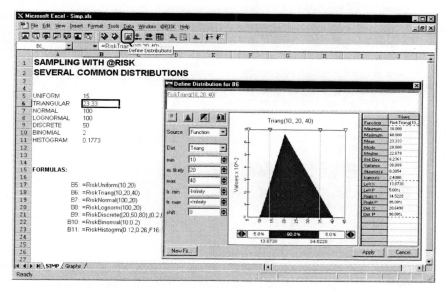

4.1.4 Select the Output Cells - Use the @RISK Toolbar

The next logical step in designing a simulation model is to select the output ranges. The main Excel menu has a choice **@RISK** and an **@RISK toolbar**.

➢ Click on the @RISK menu and you will see the following menu items. In addition, the @RISK toolbar contains icons which provide "shortcuts" to the key commands on this @RISK menu. One icon is used to select outputs. Before we actually select any outputs, we describe the other icons. Only **Add Output** and **Start Simulation** icons are necessary to run a simulation. You should select at least one output cell for @RISK to keep track of, and then you must start the simulation.

@RISK Menu and Toolbar in Excel

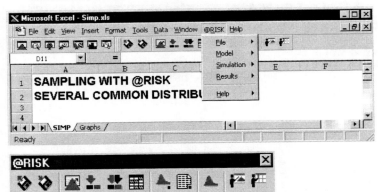

@RISK Add-in Toolbar Icons

The following icons are shown on the @RISK toolbar in Excel.

Icon   Function Performed

Open a saved @RISK simulation

Save the current @RISK simulation, including results and graphs

The **Open** and **Save** icons refer to simulation (*.RST) files. You may save the simulation files after execution. **Open** is used to retrieve the results of previous simulation runs.

Add or edit probability distributions in the formula in the current cell

The **Define Distribution** icon allows you to define a distribution graphically as opposed to typing a function directly in a cell. When you do this, you still end up with a function in your cell; however, it is automatically entered by @RISK. This was illustrated in section 4.1.3.

Icon   *Function Performed*

Add the current selected spreadsheet cell (or range of cells) as a simulation output

The **Add Output** icon allows us to designate cells or ranges of cells whose values are to be compiled during a simulation.

Display current output cell(s) along with all distribution functions entered in the worksheet in the Outputs and Inputs list

The **Display List of Outputs and Inputs** icon shows a table of all the outputs and probability distributions in your model.

Select cells in Excel containing @RISK distribution functions, output functions or statistics functions

The **Select @RISK Functions** icon highlights the cells in Excel that contain your probability distributions or outputs. This is useful for quickly finding your distributions in your worksheet.

View or change the simulation settings, including # of iterations, # of simulations, sampling type, standard recalc method, executed macros and other settings

The **Simulation Settings** icon allows a variety of simulation settings to be entered in the Settings dialog.

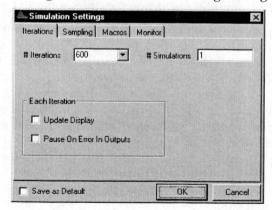

Iterations sets both the number of iterations (DEF=100) and the number of simulations (DEF=1). It is described in more detail below.

Update display: Refresh display after each iteration (DEF=don't refresh). Generally, users leave this setting off because the continual writing to the screen slows down the simulation and often happens so swiftly that you can't see the results anyhow.

Pause on Error in Outputs: Interrupt the simulation whenever any output cell yields an ERR. Default is to not pause. You will probably use this feature only rarely. @RISK does keep track of output cells that generate errors (e.g., division by 0) during simulations, and normally you let the simulation run its full cycle.

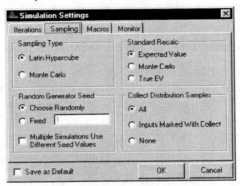

Sampling Type: **Monte Carlo** Vs **Latin Hypercube** (DEF). Elsewhere, we discuss Latin Hypercube sampling, a form of stratified sampling, which makes the simulation more efficient.

Standard Recalc chooses what appears in a worksheet cell containing a distribution function. There are three choices. The default (DEF) is the mean or **Expected Value** of the distribution. Another choice, **Monte Carlo**, yields a randomly selected value from the distribution each time the cell is recalculated.   The third choice affects only discrete distributions. As mentioned above, using the @RISK default setting of expected value produces a rounded off number for every discrete distribution. By choosing **True Expected Value**, we can avoid the round-off. With anything except discrete distributions, True Expected Value and Expected Value yield identical values.

The **Macros** tab contains options that allow you to run macros during a simulation. The **Monitor** tab allows you to monitor how "stable" the statistics on your outputs are and update graphs and statistics during a simulation.

4.1 Basics of @RISK Using Excel

Icon   Function Performed

Display reporting options

The **Report Settings** icon displays a dialog where you can select to generate simulation reports directly in Excel.

Simulate the current worksheet(s)

The **Start Simulation** icon simulates the current worksheets.

Display the Model window with outputs, inputs and fitting data

@RISK has a Model window and a Results window (along with the toolbar and menu in Excel). The **Display Model Window** icon brings up the @RISK – Model window where the outputs and distributions in your worksheet are listed and distributions can be fit to data using @RISK's built-in BestFit software.

Display the results of the most recent @RISK simulation in the Results window

The **Display Results Window** icon brings up the @RISK – Results window where graphs and reports on simulation results are displayed.

Using the @RISK Toolbar

Try the following to learn more about the icons on the @RISK toolbar:

➢ Practice the **Define Distribution** icon and select at least two of the input distribution cells and watch their probability density functions (PDFs) be constructed.

➢ Try adding outputs. Let us build two output cells with corresponding names. Type as follows.

```
B13:   =B5+B6+B7
B14:   =B5+B6+B7+B8
```

Next, provide names for these two outputs. Enter the following in your worksheet:

```
A13: Sumof3
A14: Sumof4
```

Pointing to cell B13 and click on the **Add Output** icon. Similarly, point to cell B14 and add it also.

Note: Outputs are ranges. There are some differences between single cell and multiple cell output ranges in the outputs are displayed afterwards. In particular, when data is plotted for a single cell output, a choice of a histogram or a CDF is given. For multiple cell ranges, however, the you may also display a **Summary Graph,** which takes the underlying distributions for each cell in the range and summarizes them by showing the trend of the mean values (the 10th percentile and the 90th percentile). You can access and display the individual cell distributions if you wish. The concept of trend arises because we often have a range that represents a time sequence, such as a production or economic forecast over a period of months or years, and then the mean value each year represents a trend.

➤ Click on **Simulation Settings icon** and modify one or both of the following:

 # Iterations: Change from the default of 100 to 500 iterations.

 # Simulations: In order to have more than one simulation, you must not only change the default setting for **# Simulations**, but you must also include somewhere in the worksheet a special distribution function, SIMTABLE. For example, entering `=RiskSimtable(.10,.12)` in a cell that represents interest rate, and setting Simulations to 2, would cause two sets of iterations. The first iterations would have interest rate set to 0.10, and the second set of iterations would use 0.12 for interest rate. Typically users might run 5 or 10 simulations. We will run only one simulation in the present model.

4.1.5 Run the Simulation(s)

This is a good time to save your Excel worksheet. Do so, giving it the name SIMP.XLS

➤ Click the **Start Simulation** icon to begin. You could interrupt (pause) by pressing the <Esc> key and continue if you like.

4.1.6 View the Results

In @RISK, simulation results are displayed in the @RISK – Results window. This window allows you to examine statistics and reports on the simulations just completed.

@RISK Results Window

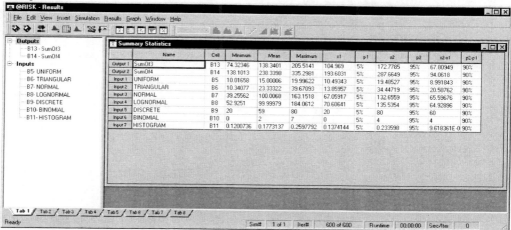

Most of the reporting and graphing options in the @RISK – Results window can be accessed using toolbars and the Explorer list on the left side of the window.

➢ Right-click on one or more output or input in the Explorer list and graph simulation results as Histograms.

The Results Window Explorer List

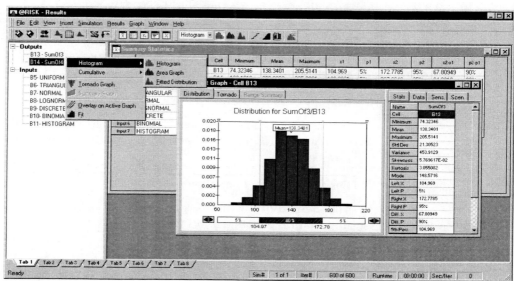

The first toolbar in the Results window is the same as the @RISK toolbar in Excel. The second – the **Insert Window** toolbar – allows you to display the different reports available on simulation results.

The third toolbar – the **Graph** toolbar – allows you to change the format of displayed graphs.

The following icons are available in the Results window:

Icon   *Function Performed and Command Equivalent*

Display summary statistics window

The **Summary Statistics** window displays the minimum, mean, and maximum values for 1) each output selected and 2) each input distribution sampled. You can also enter "target" values in this table – for example, if you wanted to find the probability of a result <=1,000,000, your target would be 1,000,000 and @RISK would show the probability of a value less than or equal to 1,000,000 occurring.

Display detailed statistics window

The **Detailed Statistics** window displays a full set of statistics on each output and input.

Display data window

The **Data** window displays, for each output, the value calculated each iteration and, for each input, the value sampled.

Display sensitivity analysis window

The **Sensitivity** window displays, for each output, the important inputs that affect results.

Display scenario analysis window

The **Scenario analysis** window displays, for each output, the groups of important inputs that lead to different results occurring. For example, when results are "high", what inputs are significant?

Graph tornado(s) of sensitivity analysis results

The **Tornado graph** icon generates a tornado graph where the most significant inputs have the longest "bars" in the tornado.

 Graph summary of simulation results for output range(s)

The **Summary graph** icon displays a "band" graph for an output range such as displayed in Figure 3.9.

 Display current graph as a histogram

Display the simulated distribution for an output or a sampled input as a histogram.

 Display current graph as an area graph

Displays a simulated distribution as an area graph with connected points at the midpoint of each histogram bar.

 Display current graph as a fitted curve

Displays a simulated distribution as a fitted curve.

 Display current graph as a cumulative ascending graph

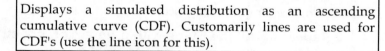 Displays a simulated distribution as an ascending cumulative curve (CDF). Customarily lines are used for CDF's (use the line icon for this).

 Display current graph as a cumulative descending line graph

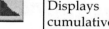 Displays a simulated distribution as a descending cumulative curve.

 Display graph format options

Displays the graph formatting dialog.

 Generate current graph as an Excel format graph

Generates the current Results window graph in Excel in standard Excel chart format.

4.1.7 Exploring the graphs

Try the following to learn more about the graphs in the @RISK Results window.

➤ Right-click on one or more outputs in the Explorer list and create histograms.

➤ Make one of the charts active. This will happen automatically when you click on a graph window or you could use the Window menu item. First convert it from a histogram with bars to an ascending CDF with lines by clicking the **Ascending Cumulative** icon on the graph toolbar.

➤ Graphs can be rescaled simply by dragging the left (minimum) or right (maximum) edge of the graph to a new minimum or maximum. With a graph represented as an ascending CDF with lines, hold down the mouse button while over an endline and drag to change the X-Minimum or X-Maximum.

➤ With one CDF "active", overlay a second CDF on top of it by right-clicking on the output to overlay in the Explorer and selecting **Overlay on Active Graph**.

➤ Copy the new combined chart to the clipboard and then paste it into the worksheet.

➤ Create an Excel-format version of a graph by making a chart active and clicking the **Graph in Excel** icon.

4.1.8 Repeating All the Steps with a New Worksheet.

Refer to AHR1.XLS, shown in Figure 3.7. Follow these instructions.

1) Either open this file or type in the cell entries for Columns A, B, and C and save the worksheet under a new name. This worksheet represents a *bona fide* application: estimating reserves for a prospect.

2) Select cell A8 and type Reserves. Select Cell B8 and click the **Add Output** icon.

3) Click the Simulation Settings icon and in **Iterations** type in 1000 and click OK.

4) Click the **List Outputs and Inputs** icon (the one with the two arrows) to display the list of all inputs and outputs in the @RISK-Model window. Right-click in the Explorer list and select **Define Distribution** to display a graph of each function.

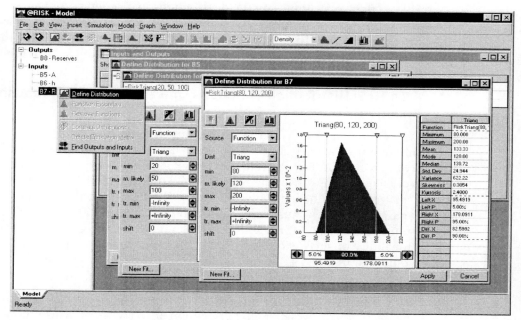

5) Click the **Start Simulation** icon to start a simulation.

6) When the run is complete, review the statistics report and generate a graph of Reserves. The positive skewness is a consequence of the fact that the formula for Reserves involves a product of distributions.

7) Insert a Data window and review the raw data.

8) Save your simulation results by selecting on **@RISK, Save.**

You should now be equipped to design a simple worksheet model for a Monte Carlo simulation and run it.

4.2 Sampling With Distribution Functions in @RISK

This section concentrates on the distributions in a generic sense and provides some examples of how to apply some distributions in the oil and gas industry. For convenience, **the =Risk-prefix is omitted from function names for the remainder of this discussion, except when necessary to point out a difference in syntax**. Upper case is used to emphasize that we are talking about special functions.

4.2.1 How Distribution Functions Differ from Other Spreadsheet Functions

The @RISK add-in contains numerous distribution functions, which behave differently from EXP, LOG, and other spreadsheet functions. EXP, for example, requires a value for its argument either explicitly or by referencing a cell in the worksheet. That is, we can evaluate EXP(2) or EXP(C5). Every time we call upon a distribution function, however, we get a random value of the corresponding random variable. Thus, if we call upon BINOMIAL(4, 0.2), we will get an integer from the set 0,1,2,3,4, representing the number of successes in 4 trials where the probability of success on each trial is 0.2. We would get more 0's and 1's than we would get 3's and 4's. For example, the probability of 3 successes is 0.0256. If we sampled 100 values from BINOMIAL(4, 0.2) and plotted their histogram, we would approximate the theoretical histogram for that binomial distribution.

This section relates back to the discussion about types of distributions in Chapter 2 and organizes some of the more commonly used distributions in Monte Carlo simulation of oil and gas applications. In each case, you can think of the process depicted in Figure 3.3, where we start with a uniformly distributed value between 0 and 1 to enter the vertical axis of the CDF of the distribution of interest.

4.2.2 Discrete Distributions Used to Estimate Odds of Successes and Failures.

Recall that discrete distributions generally *count* things, while continuous distributions tend to *measure*. Often we want to count the number of successes or compare the number of successes to the number of failures. Success might mean a commercial well, an activity completed under budget, or a satisfactory well test. Failure might mean a dry hole, a project failing to be completed on time or under budget, an instance of stuck pipe or other problems while drilling. The common ingredients of the *binomial, geometric, and negative binomial* are repeated trials and Success on a given trial has a fixed probability, p. In other words, we are *drawing with replacement*. We use the context of drilling n wildcat wells where success means a commercial well. Here are the distributions in the proper syntax along with some typical uses.

BINOMIAL(n, p)	Number of successes in n trials when p is the probability of success in each trial. Example: number of commercial wells drilling 12 wildcats with 20% success rate, assuming locations are independent, (n=12, p=0.20)
GEOMET(p)	Number of failures prior to the first success when p is the probability of success in each trial. Example: number of dry hole wildcats drilled before the first commercial well is discovered.
NEGBIN(s, p)	Number of failures prior to achieving s successes when p is the probability of success in each trial. Example: the probability distribution for drilling x non-commercial exploratory wells before the second of two commercial wells are discovered, if the probability of each well being commercial is 25%, is given by NEGBIN(2,0.25).

If we sample **without replacement**, then the appropriate counterpart of the binomial distribution is the *hypergeometric* distribution. The corresponding @RISK distribution function is

HYPERGEO(n, D, M)	Sometimes referred to as drawing without replacement. Examples:1. If you really believe that exactly 20 (=D) of the 100 (=M) locations in a given area will be successful, then this model will predict the number of successes in n trials. 2. Number of defective items in a sample from a batch where you know the proportion of bad items in the whole batch.

4.2.3 Other Distributions for Discrete Data (Historical Data)

Aside from the classic probability distributions for discrete data discussed above, we can have historical data that we wish to use as a basis for forecasting. In effect, we treat the sample as the source population and sample from it. The first four distributions below fit into this category. The last, the Poisson distribution, is an important distribution with a range of applications.

DUNIFORM($\{x_1,...,x_n\}$)	Similar to UNIFORM, but designed for discrete variables. The n events in the sample space $x_1, x_2,...,x_n$ are each assigned the probability $1/n$. Example: One toss of a fair die DUNIFORM(1,2,..,6,6)
DISCRETE($\{x_1,..,x_n\},\{p_1,...,p_n\}$)	Assigns probability to each of a finite number of distinct possibilities. Example: traditional chance node in decision tree: Big(100 MMbbl), Medium (25 MMbbl), or Small(5 MMbbl) reserves for commercial reservoir with probabilities 10%,30%,60%: DISCRETE(5,0.60,25,0.30,100,0.10,3)
POISSON (λ)	The discrete distribution describing the number of events in a measure of either distance or time when we know the probability of an event per unit of that measure. Examples: 1. Well servicing: how many weeks with 0 wells needing to be serviced when there is an average of one well serviced every two days. 2. The number of wrong number telephone calls per week when we know the average number of wrong calls per day. 3. The number of errors per printed page, or of defects per 100 feet of rolled steel. 4. The Poisson distribution is sometimes used to approximate the binomial distribution when the number of trials, n, is large and the probability of success per trial, p, is small because the Poisson is easier to compute.

4.2.4 Classic Continuous Random Variables

Continuous random variables usually represent some type of measurement such as area, thickness, fraction or percent of pore space filled with water or oil or gas, ratios of volumes (formation volume factors), decline rates, flow rates, time until an event occurs, and so on. Although not usually thought of as a measurement, prices and costs are generally modeled as continuous variables. Chapter 3 introduced four continuous distributions commonly used in oil and gas modeling: uniform, normal, triangular, and lognormal.

The uniform distribution assumes all equal-width ranges of events are equally likely, while the triangular gives less chance to events clustered at the extreme values of the sample space. The normal distribution is the well known bell shaped curve, while the lognormal distribution represents variables whose logarithms are normally distributed, a surprisingly common type of random variable. We also include the exponential distribution, which has found its way into oil and gas modeling and has numerous applications in other forms of engineering.

UNIFORM(min, max)	A very common distribution used when all possible values are equally likely. Example: reservoir properties such as net pay, water saturation, porosity, drainage radius.
TRIANG(min, mode, max)	Often used for historic data when the uniform is not appropriate, or when data is sparse. Symmetric triangular distributions have mean = median = mode. Example: porosity, net pay, water saturation, and other reservoir parameters that we suspect are closer to normally or lognormally distributed than uniformly distributed.
TRIGEN(x, ML, y, x%, y%)	Similar to TRIANG, x and y represent cutoff values below and above the mode, and x% and y% represent their respective percentages. Thus, TRIGEN(x, ML, y, 0, 100) is the same as TRIANG(x, ML, y), and TRIGEN(x, ML, y, 10, 90) is identical to TRI1090(x, ML, y).
LOGNORM (μ, σ)	Quantities that are products of several parameters, regardless of the nature of the distributions of the individual parameters. Examples 1. Reservoir volume, hydrocarbon pore volume (HCPV), recoverable hydrocarbon. 2. Permeability of wells in a reservoir. 3. Bids on parcels in a lease sale (land value estimates are thought to be the product of recoverable HC and value per bbl). 4. Average depth to target in exploration wells. 5. Discovery volume, such as ore tonnage, copper deposits.
LOGNORM2 (μ, σ)	The variables specified are the mean and standard deviation for the underlying normal distribution. By definition a random variable is lognormally distributed if the natural log of that variable is normally distributed. This formulation requires estimates of the mean and the standard deviation of that underlying normal distribution. This form is particularly suited to fitting a distribution to a sample of historical data.

NORMAL (μ, σ)	The classic symmetric, continuous distribution that describes a wide variety of naturally occurring objects. Examples: 1. Porosity, water saturation, net pay, drainage radius, etc. 2. Random errors in measurement of manufactured parts. 3. Means of samples of a given size drawn from any population. 4. The normal distribution is sometimes used to approximate the binomial distribution when the probability of success on each trial, p, is not close to either 0 or 1 and the number of trials, n, is large. In these cases, the binomial distribution is more difficult to calculate.
EXPON(β)	Time between events; such as expected lifetime of electronic devices and other products. Examples: 1. Lifetime of a drill bit (highly dependent on the environment). 2. Time to control a kick or to fish while drilling. This distribution is widely used in engineering as an approximation. For a readable account of Monte Carlo sampling using the exponential distribution, see Dhir, Dern, and Mavor (1991)

4.2.5 Continuous Distributions for Grouped Data

There are three distribution functions that lend themselves to sampling from data grouped into classes: GENERAL, CUMUL, and HISTOGRM. Each of these distributions honor the actual data, rather than assuming the data take a specific form. That is, you need not assume that your data comes from a population with a uniform, triangular, normal, or lognormal distribution. In Chapter 2, we discussed how to group historical data into classes and then build the corresponding histogram and CDF for the grouped data.

In Excel, the arguments of these distributions can be references to ranges in the worksheet. Let's examine some cases. We use the notation m and M for Minimum and Maximum, respectively in the argument lists.

CUMUL({x_1,...,x_n},{p_1,..., p_n})	Do-it-yourself cumulative distribution having n breakpoints and n+1 categories. Note: p_i <= 1. Example: 1. Any cumulative curve for historical data.
GENERAL(m,M,{x_1,...,x_n} ,{p_1,...,p_n})	Do-it-yourself probability distribution having n internal breakpoints and n+1 categories. Example: any probability curve for historical data.
HISTOGRAM(m, M, {p_1, p_2,...,p_n})	Continuous data, grouped into classes, make up this popular and useful distribution. Unlike CUMUL and GENERAL, HISTOGRM requires that the intervals (classes) be equally spaced. Examples: 1. Grouped measurements or estimates of virtually any kind: porosity, permeability, net pay, drainage area, water saturation, recovery factors, field size. 2. Grouped quantities where each category represents several distinct possibilities, such as number of layers in a stratified reservoir, grouped into 0-5, 6-10, 11-15, etc.

4.2.6 Truncated Distributions and Validity Checking

Some parameters have no practical meaning outside a particular range. Negative values of area, net pay, porosity and other measurements don't make sense. When you model these parameters with certain continuous distributions, you admit the possibility of sampling outside an acceptable range. There are essentially two ways to avoid these bogus sampled values.

A simple method for preventing unwanted values is to test every sampled value with an IF function in the spreadsheet. If the value falls outside the desired range, it is discarded. Of course, you should monitor this process carefully. Your simulation process may take averages or otherwise rely on a certain number of valid iterations. When you disqualify any iterations, calculated results like averages are subject to question.

A second method of restricting the range of sampled values is to use *truncated* distributions. Any distribution in @RISK can be truncated using the **RiskTruncate** function. RiskTruncate is added as an optional argument to any distribution such as:

```
=RiskNormal(1000,100,RiskTruncate(800,1200)
```

In this example samples will be drawn from the distribution RiskNormal(1000,100); however, no samples outside the range from a minimum of 800 to a maximum of 1200 will be allowed.

Truncation is easy to enter when defining a distribution graphically. Click the Define Distribution icon and enter the distribution and arguments you wish to use. Then, enter the truncation values for **tr.min** and **tr.max**, as shown:

Entering Truncation Graphically

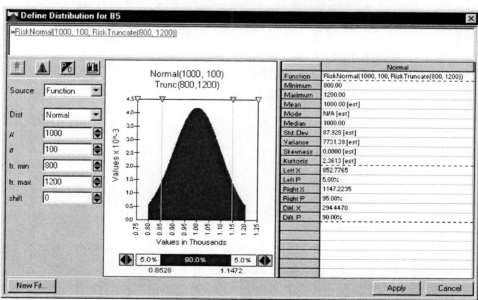

To appreciate these truncated distributions, one must bear in mind that the ranges of many distributions, such as the exponential, normal and lognormal, are infinite. That is, their probability density functions theoretically extend from $-\infty$ to $+\infty$, or 0 to $+\infty$. A normally distributed random variable with mean 100 and standard deviation 30 can actually take on values of -3000 or +900000. Of course, the probability of such extreme values is extremely small. When the parameter you wish to approximate with a normal distribution makes sense only for a restricted range, and you don't want to take the chance of sampling outside that range, you may wish to use a truncated distribution.

For example, suppose you represent porosity with a normal distribution having mean 18% and standard deviation 3%. The practical range of such a distribution is from 9% to 27%, using the rule of thumb of three standard deviations either side of the mean. To avoid small values, you could force the sampling to the interval [9%, 27%] using the distribution

```
RiskNormal(0.18,0.03,RiskTruncate(0.09,0.27)).
```

When you truncate a distribution, you alter the expected mean and standard deviation of the sample you generate. For a normal distribution, if the truncation is symmetric, the sampled values should remain evenly distributed about the original mean, but the variance will be modified. With the exponential and lognormal distributions, both the mean and standard deviation will be altered, and there is no simple way to estimate these altered parameters.

The *truncated* distributions should not be used as alternatives to the modified triangular distributions – TRIGEN. When you sample from `Trigen(0.09, 0.18,0.27,5,95)`, you are specifying a random variable that falls between 0.09 and 0.27 all except 10% of the time, when it would be outside that range. By contrast, RiskNormal(0.18,0.03,RiskTruncate(0.09,0.27)) never returns a value less that 0.09 or greater than 0.27.

4.3 Production Forecast with Simple Economics

One of the most common models in the oil and gas industry is the forecast of production and the corresponding forecast of net cash flow. This model applies to a single well, a small reservoir, or a large field. A simple version of those models are presented here along with a discussion of ways to refine the models by incorporating uncertainty. Some of the refinements are straightforward, such as replacing the two parameters of an exponential decline curve with probability distributions. Other alterations are more complex, such as handling forecasts of prices and costs. The worksheet we start with contains several organizational and stylistic features that should help us as we enhance the model.

Abundant detail for constructing the worksheet is provided, in the hope of instilling some good habits for future worksheet design. Future sections will not offer the same level of detail for commands or menu items. Rather, worksheet features will be suggested, assuming the reader knows how to implement them.

4.3.1 Features of the Worksheet

This worksheet relies on several commands and functions of Excel and introduces two @RISK features.

Worksheet features

- Absolute vs relative addresses

- Organization and documentation

- Copy command

- Data Tables

- Range Names and Range or Cell Protection

- SUM and NPV functions

- DATE function

@RISK Features

- Several distribution functions

- SIMTABLE and the ability to run more than one simulation

4.3.2 The Problems

We describe two levels of problems. The first does not include uncertainty. The second problem is more open-ended and will be left primarily to the exercises.

A. Design a template to

1) Enter a production forecast for an oil or gas well,

2) Specify parameters that describe prices and expenses, and

3) Generate a financial forecast including net present value.

B. Modify the template using distribution functions for

1) Initial flow rate and production decline rate

2) Gas-oil ratio

3) Operating costs and prices

4.3.3 Solution to Problem A.

Retrieve the worksheet DECLIN.XLS, the barebones model shown in Figure 4.1.

Figure 4.1
Worksheet
for
Exponential
Production
Decline and
Economic
Forecast

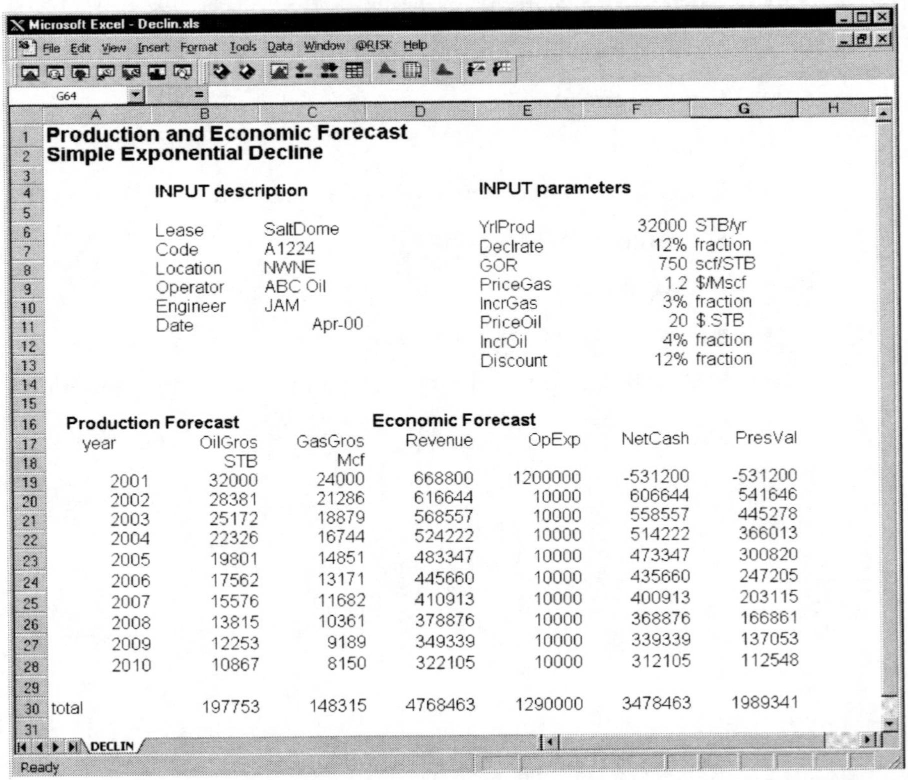

	X Microsoft Excel - Declin.xls						
	Production and Economic Forecast						
	Simple Exponential Decline						

	A	B	C	D	E	F	G
4		INPUT description			INPUT parameters		
6		Lease	SaltDome		YrlProd	32000	STB/yr
7		Code	A1224		Declrate	12%	fraction
8		Location	NWNE		GOR	750	scf/STB
9		Operator	ABC Oil		PriceGas	1.2	$/Mscf
10		Engineer	JAM		IncrGas	3%	fraction
11		Date		Apr-00	PriceOil	20	$.STB
12					IncrOil	4%	fraction
13					Discount	12%	fraction

	Production Forecast			Economic Forecast			
year		OilGros	GasGros	Revenue	OpExp	NetCash	PresVal
		STB	Mcf				
2001		32000	24000	668800	1200000	-531200	-531200
2002		28381	21286	616644	10000	606644	541646
2003		25172	18879	568557	10000	558557	445278
2004		22326	16744	524222	10000	514222	366013
2005		19801	14851	483347	10000	473347	300820
2006		17562	13171	445660	10000	435660	247205
2007		15576	11682	410913	10000	400913	203115
2008		13815	10361	378876	10000	368876	166861
2009		12253	9189	349339	10000	339339	137053
2010		10867	8150	322105	10000	312105	112548
total		197753	148315	4768463	1290000	3478463	1989341

| **Documentation and Organization** | This worksheet is designed to be easily adaptable to stochastic modeling. Descriptive information appears in Cells B6..C11, with Column C containing user inputs. The input cells are highlighted for easy reference. |

Input parameters appear in Cells F6..F13, and their names and units flank them in Columns E and G. One other input is the forecast starting year in A19. All other cells in the table contain formulas that reference the input cells.

Model Assumptions

1) *Exponential* decline pattern for the oil:

$$q = q_i * exp(-at)$$

where q_i is the annual production for the first year and a is the (fixed) annual percentage decline rate

2) *Constant gas-oil-ratio, GOR,* which is a user input

3) *Prices escalate at fixed annual percentages,* which are user inputs. The formulas in Column D multiply initial year price by the factor $(1+s)^{n-1}$ where n is the number of years forward in the forecast and s is the annual fractional increase of either the oil or gas price.

4) ABC Oil Company owns a 100% share of this property.

5) *Operating expenses are fixed* throughout the forecast. The first year expense may be thought of as capital investment.

Getting Started

Ranges to Name: Columns B and E contain names for adjacent cells in Columns C and F

Highlight B6:C11, Click on **Formula, Create Names, Left Column**; Do same for E6:F13

Formulas to type and copy:

Column A: one input cell, A19, the starting year.

Cell A20: `=A19+1`. Copy this down.

Columns B and C: oil and gas forecasts for 10 years. The exponential decline formula was entered in Cell B19, being careful to use absolute references for F6 and F7, and copied down through the column. In C19, an absolute reference, F8, was used for the constant GOR. Incidentally, under normal depletion of an oil reservoir, unless there is significant pressure maintenance, the GOR would increase significantly after the reservoir pressure fell below bubble point and gas saturation began to increase.

Column D:

Revenue = (oil production) x (oil price) + (gas production) x (gas price).

Annual compounding of price was introduced using $(1+\$IncrOil)^{\wedge}(n-1)$ and $(1+\$IncrGas)^{\wedge}(n-1)$. Note how we accomplish this "n-1" exponent by using the expression A19-A19 for the first year and copying it downward. Subsequent rows yield A20-A19, A21-A19, etc., which is the sequence 1,2,...

Column E: fixed annual operating expense, with capital investment for the first year

Column F: subtract operating expense from Column F

Column G: divide each entry in H by $(1+\$Discount)^{\wedge}(n-1)$ to get (end-of year) discounted cash flow

Totals - the SUM Function. You can type in Cell B30:

```
=SUM(B19:B28)
```

and then copy across Row 30 (Copying will carry formats with it).

4.3 4 Using the Worksheet

So far, the worksheet has no uncertainty built in. Each parameter estimates consists of a single deterministic value. Prices will change from year to year, but in a completely predictable fashion. The production forecast is completely determined once we input the values in Cells F6 and F7. Likewise, the economic forecast is determined as soon as we specify the values in Cells F6..F13 and the operating expense column. We can alter the value in one of the input cells and watch the effect on the NPV (the sum of the discounted cash flow column, G30). This is a fairly unsophisticated form of sensitivity testing.

This model cries out for some form of *uncertainty*. Does the well have a known initial potential and a known decline? Can we predict the exact forecast of prices? Are operating expenses known, much less fixed? The following exercises will allow you to explore these matters, both in the worksheet and using @RISK.

4.3.5 Exercises

1. Spend some time changing the input parameters to see how they affect the total net present value. In particular, alter the discount rate to find one that will yield a value of $0 in Cell I28. That discount rate is the Internal Rate of Return (IRR) or the Discounted Cash Flow Return On Investment (DCFROI).

2. (Intermediate to advanced spreadsheet users) Use the Data Table command to estimate the DCFROI. First build a column for variable discount rates ranging from 10% to 90%. Put the reference =G30 in the cell immediately to the right of and one cell above the top of that column. The two column range shown below will be the range for a one-parameter data table. Use the commands Data Table to get started. The column entries refer to Cell F13, the discount rate. You objective is to find (by trial and error) the discount rate that yields a 0 for NPV, the values appearing in the second column of the table.

	G30
0.1	
0.2	
0.3	
0.4	
0.5	
0.6	
0.7	
0.8	
0.9	

3. *Adding uncertainty to the production forecast.* Begin with DECLIN.XLS, and assign distribution functions to the following three parameters in Column F:

```
F6:    NORMAL(32000,8000)
F7:    NORMAL(0.12,0.02)
F8:    TRIANG(500,750,1500)
```

Note that the *mean* of the triangular distribution for GOR is 917 although its *mode* is 750. This leads to a discrepancy in the gas column between the new worksheet and the original DECLIN.XLS.

a) Run a simulation using all default values for @RISK. Select G30 as the sole Output cell.

---

b) Run a simulation using the Oil Gros column as an output range, naming it Oil Gros. Right-click on the output range Oil Gros in the Explorer and select Summary Graph. This will result in a Summary Graph similar to the one in Figure 3.9.

To graph a distribution for simulation results for a single cell in the output range, highlight the desired cell in the Explorer, right-click and choose and choose the type of graph you wish to view, such as **Histogram.**

4. *Adding noise to a production forecast.* Start over with DECLIN.XLS and re-solve Problem B (posed at the beginning of this section) as follows. In the OilGros column, alter the formulas by multiplying each by NORMAL(1,0.10). Explain how to interpret this change. You might want to do a similar thing for the expenses column, including the first year, which includes drilling and completion costs. Run the simulation with both the NPV and the gross oil column as outputs. By saving a copy of the graphs from Problem 3 (by copying and pasting the graph into your worksheet or by using the **Graph in Excel** command), you can compare Problem 4's Summary Graph with that of Exercise 3.

5. *Adding uncertainty to prices.* One method of imposing uncertainty on prices is to introduce distribution functions for both the gas and oil annual price increments:

```
F10:   TRIANG(-0.02, 0.02, 0.05)
F12:   TRIANG(-0.02, 0.04, 0.06)
```

The problem with this method is that the same increment is used each year in the forecast. More realistically, each year might have a different price change (up or down) represented by some random variable. The real question becomes, how would you modify prices of oil and gas to model a steady increasing trend with a lot of variation?

One way is to start with the old formula and multiply each year's price by NORMAL(1, 0.1) or TRIANG(0.9, 1.0, 1.2) to add some noise to the prices. Another method, which forces each year's price to be based on the previous year's price, is to take last year's price and multiply it by two factors. One factor would represent an increasing trend, such as (1+ $IncrOil), and another factor would represent uncertainty, such as a normal or triangular distribution with mode of 1.00. How does this differ from the previous suggestion? How could you see the difference?

6. *Comparing discount rates using* SIMTABLE. @RISK allows the user to run several cases back to back. Each case is called a Simulation and the number of simulations is set using the **Simulations#** option in the Simulation Settings dialog box. To demonstrate this concept, suppose we want to compare the discounted cash flow forecasts (Column G) for different discount rates. One method is to replace the 0.12 value in Cell F13 with

```
=RiskSimtable({0.08, 0.12, 0.16, 0.20, 0.24})
```

and then specify 5 for **Simulations#**. If you have 300 iterations set in @RISK, when you click the **Start Simulation** icon, the first 300 iterations will use 0.08 for a discount rate. Then another 300 iterations will be run using a discount rate of 0.12, followed by another 300 iterations using 0.16, and so on.

The results of all five simulations require some care to explain, especially for a multi-cell range, like the oil forecast. You can view either a single summary graph that includes all simulations or individual summary graphs for each simulation. By right-clicking on the name of the output range in the Explorer and selecting Summary Graph, you can select the type of summary graph you wish to see. The summary graphs shown here resulted from specifying the cells G19:G28 as outputs, naming them Present Value, and rerunning the simulation.

Summary Graph from Multiple Simulations

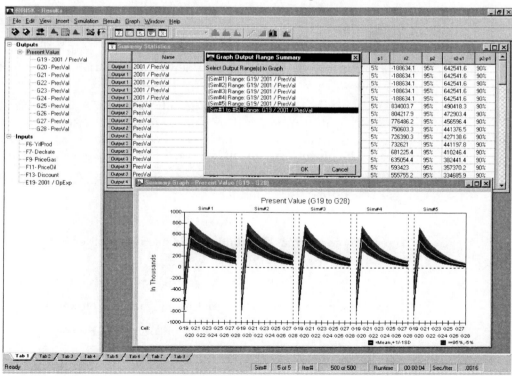

4.4 Volumetric Models – the Lognormal Distribution

By definition, a random variable, X, has a lognormal distribution if ln(X) is normally distributed. Just as there are numerous applications of normal distributions, there are a surprising number of situations where lognormal distributions occur naturally. In oil and gas modeling, we see this distribution in reservoir volumes, reserves, recoverable hydrocarbons, permeabilities, grain size distributions, and bids on parcels in lease sales. Insurance companies use the lognormal distribution to model claims. Environmentalists model pollution levels with lognormal distributions.

The first part of this section appeals to some laws of probability and statistics to help explain why lognormal distributions are so common. Then we review two @RISK distribution functions for modeling the lognormal distribution. Finally, we examine a worksheet that demonstrates how products are tend to be lognormally distributed but sums tend to be normally distributed. In the exercises, we introduce several particular applications of lognormal distributions in the oil and gas industry.

4.4.1 Background: Sums of Random Variables and a Property of Logarithms

A. Let X and Y be independent random variables, with means mx and my and variances vx and vy. We can form a new random variable X+Y, whose mean is mx + my and whose variance is vx + vy

B. If X and Y are independent identically distributed, normal random variables, then X+Y is also normally distributed. In fact, X+Y tends to normal in shape regardless of what type distributions X and Y happen to be. When more than two terms are involved, the sum tends toward a normal shape even more so.

One of the key properties of logarithms is that the log of a product is the sum of the logs of the factors. Symbolically,

$$\ln(AB) = \ln(A) + \ln(B) \tag{4.2}$$

To see why lognormal distributions are useful, consider the classic formula for oil in place.

$$OIP = 7758\ Ah\ \varphi\ (1-S_w)/B_o \tag{4.3}$$

Notice what happens if we take (natural) logarithms of both sides.

$$\ln(OIP) = \ln(7758) + \ln(A) + \ln(h) + \ln(\varphi) + \ln(1-S_w) - \ln(B_o) \tag{4.4}$$

Even though the individual components, $\ln(A)$, $\ln(h)$, $\ln(\varphi)$, $\ln(1-S_w)$, and $\ln(B_o)$, are not normally distributed, their sum $\ln(OIP)$ would tend to be.

The point is that many variables we study can be viewed as products of other variables. Often, the distributions of those products are skewed heavily in one direction. By taking logarithms of the products, the transformed variables tend to have a normal shape. Moreover, we can estimate key parameters, particularly the mean and standard variation, of these transformed variables as a first step to describing the original variable.

Among examples of parameters that are products of other parameters are reserves and resources that are the result of a volumetric formula. Another example is probability of geologic success, which is the product of probabilities of several events such as existence of a trap, source rock, or favorable timing and migration.

Even for variables like permeability, which may not appear on the surface to be the product of other variables, can be modeled as lognormal distributions. Here is one explanation. For a portion of a reservoir to exhibit high permeability, several factors have to be at work. For instance, no barriers such as shale streaks, faults, or other heterogeneities, can be present. Secondly, there must be favorable fluid saturations to offer good relative permeability. Finally, there must be reasonably uniform grain size to avoid pore throat restrictions. Whenever "all the stars have to be in the right place" for a variable to have a relatively large value, there is a good chance for that variable to exhibit a lognormal shaped distribution.

4.4.2 Two Distribution Functions, LOGNORM and LOGNORM2

@RISK has two forms of lognormal distribution functions,

> LOGNORM(M,S) specifies a lognormal distribution having mean M and standard deviation, S, and

> LOGNORM2(m,s) specifies a lognormal distribution X, whose associated distribution, ln(X), has mean m and standard deviation s. You will explore these two functions in the exercises, but for now we want to create lognormal distributions by taking products.

We will examine several cases involving products to see just how this process works. Let us begin with a simple worksheet that compares sums and products as well as comparing two simple distributions. Later, we examine several similar models pertaining to volumetric estimates of reserves.

4.4.3 Worksheet to Compare Sums and Products

The worksheet LGNRM. XLS is shown in Figure. 4.2. You may either retrieve it or reconstruct it as described below by entering the labels, the @RISK distribution functions in the "formula table" and sum and product formulas in row D . The range table in columns F and G should be used to designate the four cells (A9, B9, C9, and D9) as outputs for the simulation.

Figure 4.2
Worksheet to
Calculate
Sums and
Products of
Distributions

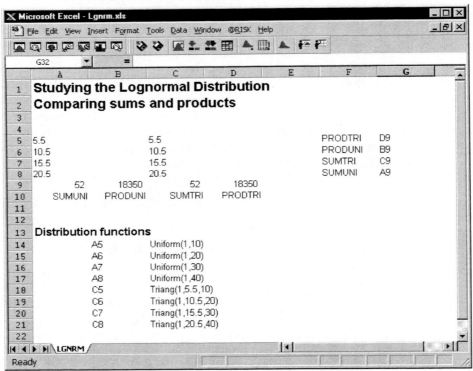

The objective is to calculate both the sum and product of four independent variables and to describe their distributions. Further, we want to see how the choice of distributions for the individual factors might affect the sum and product. For this purpose, we compare the uniform and the triangular distributions, the former having much larger dispersion that the latter.

Distributions   Cells A5 to A8 contain Uniform distributions. Cells C5 to C8 contain similar Triangular distributions. Ranges, means, and standard deviations have been selected with similar orders of magnitude so that no one distribution would dominate the others.

Cells A9 and C9 contain the sums of the 4 cells above. Cells B9 and D9 contain the corresponding products. From the earlier discussion, we anticipate the products to

---

yield approximately lognormal distributions and the sums to yield approximately normal distributions.

@RISK Settings

Experience will reveal that experiments like these often require large numbers of trials for the output distributions to smooth out. Probability theory tells us the same thing. Since this is a minimal worksheet to begin with, we will be generous and click the **Simulation Settings** icon and set **# Iterations** at 2000. We use the **Add Output** icon to assign the four cells in Row 9, SUMUNI, PRODUNI, SUMTRI, and PRODTRI, as simulation outputs.

Running @RISK and Viewing the Results

Begin the iterations by clicking the **Start Simulation** icon. After the simulation is complete, take a quick look at each of the four outputs. Your graphs should resemble those in Fig. 4.3. You may want to compare the two sums output cells by first using Zoom/Rescale to give them common X and Y scales and then copy one and overlay it on the other. You should see a marked contrast between the two distributions, both of which should appear to be somewhat normal in shape. In particular, SUMUNI should be far more dispersed (i.e., it should have a much larger standard deviation).

Figure. 4.3   Comparing Sums and Products of Distributions

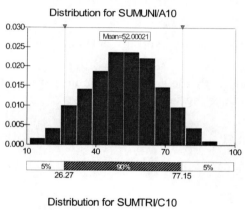

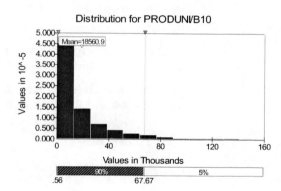

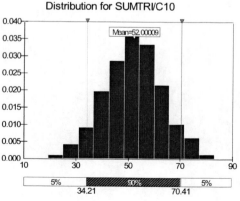

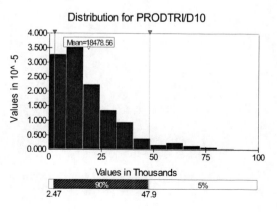

Similarly, you should overlay the two product output cells. Again the results show that PRODUNI has far more dispersion than PRODTRI. Both of these outputs, however, should appear to be highly skewed to the right, characteristic of a lognormally distributed variable.

4.4.4 Exercises

Try at least one of the following simple modifications with LGNRM.XLS before going to the next worksheets.

1. Replace the products in Cells B9 and D9 with their natural logarithms.

> Cell B9: =LN(A5*A6*A7*A8)   and similarly for D9

How do you think these values should be distributed? Find out by first deleting the current outputs in the @RISK – Model window (by right-clicking on the output range in the Explorer and selecting **Delete Outputs**) and then add only B9 and D9 as outputs. You can also delete an output by removing the RiskOutput function from an output cell. Every output cell is identified to @RISK by a RiskOutputfunction, such as:

```
=RiskOutput("ProdTri")+LN(A5*A6*A7*A8)
```

For a good comparison with your previous run, specify 2000 iterations again and execute the simulation.

2. Replace the Uniform distributions with their Normal counterparts and select only Cells A9 and B9 as outputs to reduce the simulation time.

4.4 Volumetric Models the Lognormal Distribution

3. In a clean worksheet, use five cells to contain the distribution functions, LOGNORM(100,N) where N takes on the values 20, 40, 60, 80, 100 and five more cells for LOGNORM2(5,M), where M takes on values 0.01, 0.05, 0.1, 0.5, and 1. Select all 10 of these cells for Outputs, naming them LOG20, LOG40, etc. You won't need as many iterations to see the pattern emerge; 300 should be adequate. Run the simulation and examine the results. Now save all the simulated data in case you want to do the next exercise. A quick way to get a report on all the data is to:

Click the **Report Settings** icon and select **Outputs Data** and **Inputs Data**, and click the **Generate Reports Now** button.

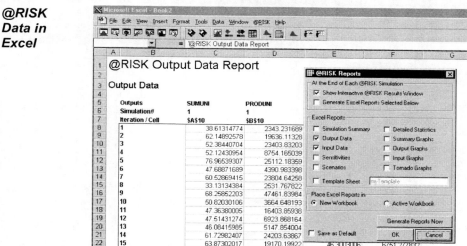

4. (Advanced) Get the data from Exercise 3:

Get the worksheet generated when you captured the data.

Take the column corresponding to one of the LOGNORM cells and insert a column to its right where you will take the natural logs of those numbers. Above that column in two cells, use the spreadsheet functions, AVG(range of natural logs) and STD(same range), to get a feel for the size of the standard deviation. Then build a new function LOGNORM2(m, s) using the average (m) and the standard deviation (s) you just calculated. This new function should generate values essentially the same as the original LOGNORM function whose data you analyzed. Verify this equivalence by running another simulation selecting only those two distributions and overlaying their CDF's.

When you have actual data that you suspect is lognormally distributed, you can take the natural logs of those data and build the LOGNORM2 distribution using the mean and standard deviation of the logs. The resulting distribution should be a good approximation to your original data.

For a more formal description of the relationship between the mean and standard deviation of a lognormally distributed variable and the mean and standard deviation of the natural log of that variable, consult the @RISK *User's Guide* or a book on probability and statistics. For a more sophisticated method of finding the best fitting lognormal distribution to a set of data, you might want to use the **Model Fit Distributions to Data** command on the @RISK menu in Excel. In this case @RISK will find the best distribution to fit your data, as shown below:

Fitting Distributions to Data in @RISK

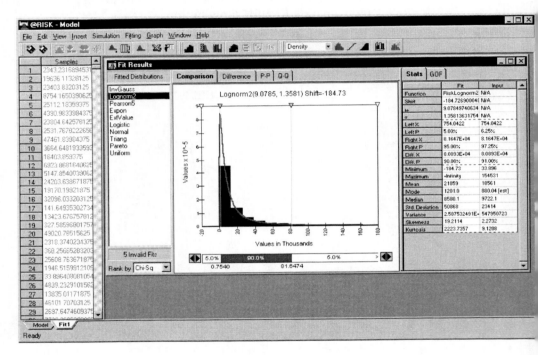

4.4 Volumetric Models the Lognormal Distribution

5. Examine COALBED.XLS (Fig 4.4) and HORIZ. XLS (Fig. 4.5). Both worksheets represent reserve estimates that involve products of variables. Experiment with them, increasing the number of iterations until the results appear to be stable. Also discuss the choices of distributions and try some alternatives. Finally, how could you incorporate SIMTABLE into these models?

Figure 4.4 A Product Model to Estimate Coalbed Methane Reserves

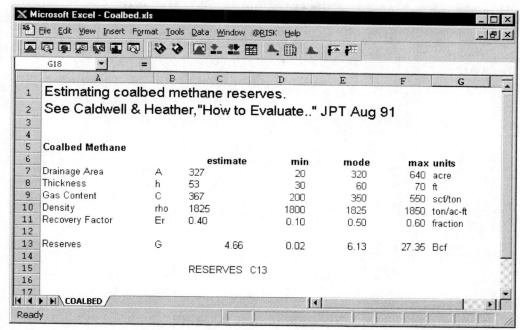

People often disagree about how many iterations to use. Deciding how many iterations is like deciding when to stop generating more digits in long division, except the process takes longer. In other words, Monte Carlo simulation is a converging process. The simplest rule is to run enough iterations so that you cannot tell the difference – or the difference is inconsequential – between output CDF's if you did any more iterations.

When designing an important model, you should test it for adequate number of iterations. Start with 300 or 400 and increase by factors of 2 or 4. Identify an important, single-cell output. At each step, overlay the CDF for this output with its counterpart for the previous number of trials until you are satisfied that further increases in iterations would yield no changes in the CDF. Obviously, there is a tradeoff. With complex worksheets, you may not have the time to run thousands of iterations. While you are learning, it is a good idea to rerun these simple models get a feel for the improvement likely by doubling or quadrupling the number of iterations.

*Figure 4.5.
A Product
Model to
Estimate
Reserves
from
Horizontal
Wellbore*

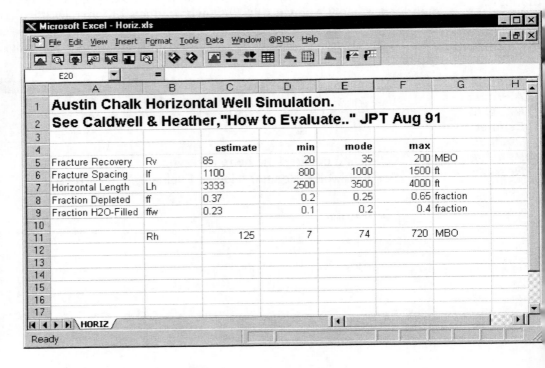

4.5 Porosity and Saturation Model – Built-in Dependency

We have noted previously that porosity and water saturation are parameters often thought to be negatively correlated. These variables appear in a variety of models and they are among the data generally available for individual completion intervals as well as reservoirs. This section examines a process of estimating porosity and water saturation from electric well logs. The purpose is two-fold. First, we see how the equations that convert raw wireline log measurements into water saturation and porosity values actually impose a relationship between those two parameters. Second, we compare the effects of using uniform versus triangular distributions to generate the estimates. Along the way, we rely on several useful features of both spreadsheets and @RISK. Indeed, we benefit from the combined use of the spreadsheet and the Monte Carlo simulation.

4.5.1 @RISK and Spreadsheet Features Used

@RISK Features

- TRIANG and UNIFORM distributions

- Copying and overlaying to compare both histograms and CDF's

- Zoom/Rescale to set common scales on graphs to be compared

Spreadsheet Features

- Regression and Correlation commands

- Graphical features

4.5.2 Problem Statement

Given estimates of bulk density and true formation resistivity from logs, we want to estimate formation porosity and water saturation. This problem can focus on either an interval in a given wellbore or on a reservoir with several well penetrations where we hope to describe average formation properties throughout the reservoir.

Our job is to assign distribution functions to each of several parameters, including the bulk density and formation resistivity, and then deduce corresponding distributions for porosity, formation factor, and water saturation.

This problem was introduced by Walstrom et al.(1967) and discussed in McCray(1975). We use McCray's values for comparison, and then modify the input distributions to see the effect.

4.5.3 Model and Input Variables

The model to convert log data to derived reservoir parameters features three equations:

$$\varphi = \frac{\rho_B - \rho_{MA}}{\rho_F - \rho_{MA}} \qquad \text{Porosity} \qquad (4.5)$$

$$F = a\varphi^{-m} \qquad \text{Formation factor} \qquad (4.6)$$

$$S_w = (FR_w / R_t)^{1/n} \quad \text{Water saturation} \qquad (4.7)$$

The input variables and their ranges of values are given below. Our objective is to estimate φ and S_w.

			min	max
R_t	=	True formation resistivity	19	21
R_w	=	Water resistivity	0.055	0.075
n	=	Archie saturation exponent	1.8	2.2
a	=	Archie coefficient	0.62	0.62
m	=	Archie cementation exponent	2	2.3
ρ_B	=	Bulk density	2.36	2.38
ρ_{MA}	=	Rock matrix density	2.58	2.63
ρ_F	=	Reservoir fluid density	0.9	0.9

At first, follow the pattern suggested by Walstrom and let each range be represented by a uniform distribution. Thus, ρ_{MA} is uniformly distributed between 2.58 and 2.63 g/cc. Next, select values for each of the eight input parameters and then calculate φ, F, and S_w in that order.

For contrast, also set up a parallel case, using triangular distributions for each of the non-constant parameters, and compare the (graphical) results. Thus, for the base case, represent R_t by UNIFORM(19, 21). Then use the symmetric triangular distribution, TRIANG(19, 20, 21). Similarly, use both UNIFORM(2.36, 2.38) and TRIANG(2.36, 2.37, 2.38) for ρ_B, bulk density.

4.5.4 Worksheet Design And @RISK Settings

Figure 4.6 shows the worksheet PHISW. XLS. All input and output parameters are listed in a column with their variable names just to the left of the cells containing values.

**Figure 4.6
Worksheet
to Calculate
Porosity
and Water
Saturation**

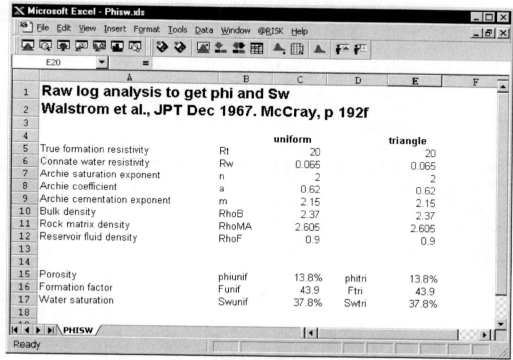

Now type in the appropriate distribution functions in Columns C (for uniform) and E (for triangular). Below input parameters in Column C, type in the three formulas (4.5, 4.6, and 4.7) listed above. Then copy those formulas to column E. This design allows us to name those parameters.

Highlight B5:C12 and click on **Insert Names Create** and select **Left Column**

Select four **Outputs,** Phiunif, Phitri, Swunif, and Swtri. Set **#Iterations** to 500.

Click the **Start Simulation** icon.

4.5.5 Results And Exercises

After the simulation is complete, step through the four output ranges (each is a single cell in this model). We have an opportunity to compare the results of uniform input parameters to triangular input parameters by copying and overlaying graphs. To do so requires some preliminary work.

4.5.6 Comparing Histograms

A quick method of comparing two distributions is to compare their histograms. View the histogram for the variable Phitri, the porosity resulting from choices of triangular distributions for each of the input variables. Overlay it on Phiunif by making a graph of Phiunif and right-clicking on Phitri in the Results Window Explorer and selecting **Overlay on Active Graph**.

4.5.7 Comparing Cumulative Distributions

A more common way of comparing two distributions is to plot their CDF's on the same axes, using the same scale. Right-click on Swtri in the Explorer and select **Cumulative – Descending Cumulative Line**. Then, right click on Swunif and select **Overlay on Active Graph**. The result should resemble Figure 4.7.

Figure 4.7 Comparing CDF's for Sw Calculation, Triangular vs Uniform Distributions

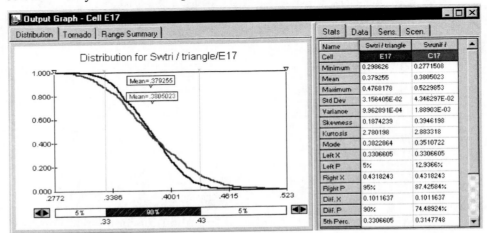

The overall result is quite plausible: using triangular distributions for each of the input variables causes a much steeper CDF. This behavior would be more obvious for models where the output variables were either sums or products of the inputs. Our model involves exponential functions, roots, and rational functions. Nevertheless, it should seem reasonable that when we assign more probability to values of the input variables close to their means, which is what happens with the triangular distribution compared to the uniform, the output variables reflect the same pattern. To put it differently, when the inputs have less uncertainty (as measured by the variance), so do the outputs.

You may also want to examine the **Statistics** for the outputs. In particular, the standard deviation and variance for Phiunif and Swunif should be appreciably larger than those of their counterparts, Phitri and Swtri.

4.5 Porosity and Saturation Model Built-in Dependency

4.5.8 Further Exercises

1. Extend the worksheet in Figure 4.7 with a new column (Column G) in which you use normal distributions for the input variables. Now it becomes necessary to select a value for the standard deviation. Recalling that virtually all of the sampled values of a normally distributed variable fall within three standard deviations (either side) of the mean, you can set the standard deviation equal to 1/3 of the distance from the mean to the either the upper or lower limit, since these distributions are symmetric. Once you have the distributions in place, you can copy the formulas from Cells E15..E17 and invent new names for cells F15..F17. In @RISK, add two new output cells, F15 and F17. Make a new simulation run and compare the resulting CDF's. The normal inputs should reduce the standard deviations of the outputs even more than the triangular inputs do.

2. Examine the relationship between the values of porosity and water saturation generated in the simulation. The functional dependence, indirectly via the formation factor, should lead to data that exhibits statistical dependence, i.e., correlation. For now, we will examine the raw data by constructing a cross plot. Follow these steps which are similar to Exercise 4 of Section 4.4:

> Click **Reports Settings** icon, select **Outputs Data** and **Inputs Data**, and click **Generate Reports Now** to generate a new worksheet with the data.

Create a graph (i.e., a crossplot) of Swtri vs Phitri and name it PHISWTRI. Create another crossplot showing Swunif vs Phiunif, and name it PHISWUNI. How would you characterize the plots in terms of dependency? Check Figure 3.15, where we combined dependence and distribution type to get four contrasting cross plots. Figure 4.8 shows the PHISWUNI cross plot for a relatively small number of iterations, along with the regression line from the next exercise.

Figure 4.8 Cross Plot, Porosity and Water Saturation Generated Using Uniform Distributions

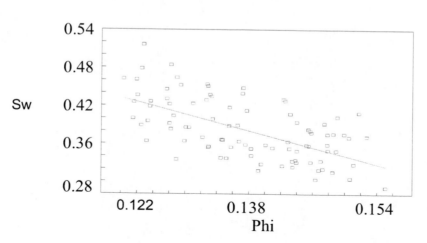

3. Estimate the degree of dependency between the two pairs of data retrieved in Problem 2. Use Phitri as the X (independent) variable and Swtri as the Y (dependent) variable. Repeat the regression with Phiunif and Swunif.

Use **Tools Add-ins Analysis Toolpak** (an Add-in), then select **Tools Data Analysis Correlation** or **Regression**. First you will have to rearrange the columns in the table of data to have the XY-pairs adjacent.

Compare the values of r-squared. You should get r-squared values in the range 0.25 to 0.35. The value of r, the correlation coefficient, is found by taking the square root of r-squared and attaching the sign of the coefficient from the regression output. Remember that the coefficient is the slope of the regression line. A downward trend signifies a negative correlation, and a positive slope signifies a positive correlation. The magnitude of the slope has no bearing of the degree of dependency between the two variables.

Typical (absolute) values of correlation coefficient, r, for field data might range from 0.20 to 0.50. There is a paucity of literature showing actual data and statistical analysis except for perennial favorites like field size. See the papers by Holtz (1993) and Murtha (1993). Of course, is you have access to field data whose parameters are among the ones you want to include in your models, then you should run regression analysis or simply use the Excel function =CORREL to find the correlation coefficient wherever possible to begin to get a feel for this important topic.

4.6 Scheduling and Timing Models

Scheduling and timing issues refer to the allocation of capital and other resources over time as well as to the generation of revenue. How much money should be invested in seismic data acquisition, platforms, facilities, pipelines, and drilling? How do we spread out these investments over time? To what degree are the schedules dependent on anticipated volumes of recovery? What will the production profile look like? Are there stages to consider such as primary depletion, waterflood, enhanced production? This section addresses some of the many time-dependent inputs to a comprehensive investment model. Needless to say, the uncertainty issues involved in such matters can be challenging to quantify.

4.6.1 Linking Investment Schedules to Field Size

Timing of capital investment is one of the more significant factors in determining a net cash flow profile. Whether for exploration or production purposes, a model representing an investment prospect is incomplete until it accounts for scheduling of investments and expenses. To be consistent, if you model the volume of recoverable hydrocarbon using distributions for input parameters, it makes sense to incorporate uncertainty in both the magnitude and scheduling of expenditures.

Straightforward methods for accounting for uncertainty in prices and operating expenses were introduced in Section 4.3. Now we will show how to add a dimension of uncertainty to scheduling.

4.6.2 Worksheet Design for Scheduling Model

Retrieve the worksheet SCHED1.XLS shown in Figure 4.9. The objective is to link both capital expenditures and the drilling schedule to the estimated size of a discovered field, or more precisely to the volume of reserves. At the top left of the worksheet (Cells A6..C9), is a simple reserve estimation using area, net pay and a recovery factor. Below are two tables: CAPEX Schedule and Drilling Schedule.

Figure 4.9 Worksheet to Impose Uncertainty on CAPEX and Drilling Schedule

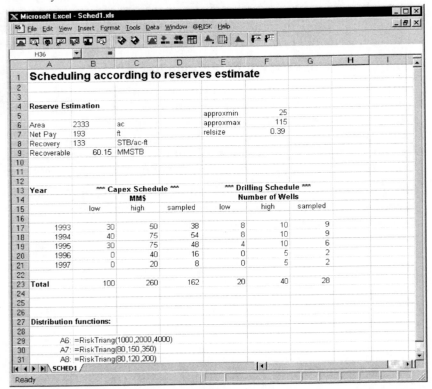

The distributions for Area, Net Pay and Recovery (factor) are all triangular, as shown in the formula table. After deciding on the distributions to model field size, a preliminary run was made selecting Recoverable (i.e., reserves) as the output. Estimates of P5 and P95 (the 5% and 95% probability levels in the CDF) of 25 MMbbl and 115 MMbbl were found. That is, only 5% of the time would reserves be less than 25MMbbl and only 5% of the time would reserves be more than 115 MMbbl. Returning to the worksheet, these two "extreme" values were used as limits for an interpolation process, calling them "approxmin" and "approxmax" in Cells F5 and F6. Then we found the relative size of the field compared to these two extremes by taking a ratio in Cell F7.

relsize = (sampled recoverable - min)/(max-min)

The actual formula in F7 is

```
=MIN(1,MAX(0,(N-F5)/(F6-F5)))
```

Thus, we found the ratio, then made sure it was between 0 and 1. Because we used P5 and P95 as cutoff values for field size, every once in a while (10 % of the time) the field size sampled will fall outside the range from approxmin to approxmax. We forced relsize, however, to always be at least 0.0 and at most 1.00. As described next, this insured that we would always calculate interpolated values in D17..D21.

Thus, for a relatively small field, we would plan a modest CAPEX and a modest drilling schedule. Likewise for a large field, we would anticipate a larger CAPEX and a more wells to be drilled. The particular estimates for the quantities (of CAPEX and wells) is not the whole story. We also need to know the timing of the expenditures and the drilling activity. All those combinations are included in the four columns titled "low" and "high" – one each for CAPEX and Drilling.

Our model assumes that any discovery in between the two extremes should correspond to schedules of investment and drilling proportional to the field size. We capture that proportionality with the ratio relsize. We implement it by interpolating both schedules for each year. Thus, Cell D17 has the formula

```
=B17 + relsize * (C17 - B17)
```

When relsize is 0, this expression reduces to B17, the "low" case. When relsize is 1.0, the expression yields the "high" case, C17. This interpolated value (you may think of it as a weighted average also) will always give us a number in between the "low" and "high" values. Thus, the sum of D17..D21 will always lie between the sums of B17..B21 and C17..C21. Column G is handled the same way. In fact, if you type the formula in Cell D17, being sure to use an absolute reference for relsize, you can copy the formula down D18..D21 and also to G17..G21.

4.6.3 Running the Scheduling Worksheet

Now that we have the basic setup for the schedules, what can we learn from a simulation? What ranges should we select? Try running a simulation with 500 iterations, selecting output ranges of Recoverable oil, CAPEX schedule, Total CAPEX, Drilling schedule, and Total number of wells. For the two schedule ranges, the results in the @RISK – Results window will be displayed as Summary Graphs, similar to the ones shown in Figure 4.10.

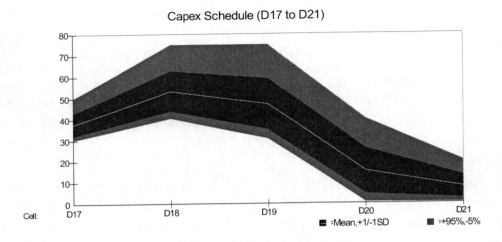

Figure 4.10
Summary
Graphs for
CAPEX and
Drilling
Schedules

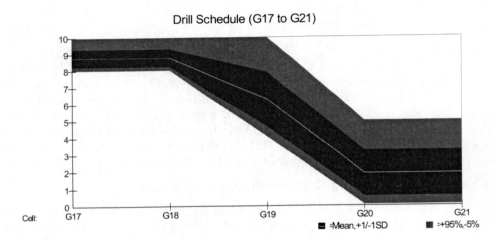

4.6.4 Shortcomings of the Scheduling Model

The interpolation scheme used here may not be an adequate representation of reality. Any (linear) interpolation assumes a **continuous** and **approximately linear** relationship between the two variables involved. In other words, we are making an implicit assumption that as field size increases, the amount of capital investment grows proportionally, as do the number of wells necessary for development. In fact, there may be stages of development (e.g., "build another platform") that could cause abrupt increases in investment. The number of wells may also be tied to the number of platforms or other physical constraints. There may be economies of scale, which mean that capital investment does not rise in proportion to field size.

Another simplification in this scheduling model is the aggregation of capital investment rather than identifying several categories (exploration, platforms, pipelines other facilities, development drilling, and so on.) Rather than being kept in lockstep, these components may require different timing schedules as well.

Another aspect of the problem has been ignored completely. The number of wells required to produce a field depends on at least two factors: the size of the field and the productive capacity of individual wells. In more comprehensive models, there some method of capturing well productivity (perhaps in the form of a decline curve with uncertainty). The combination of total reserves and capacity of the wells would dictate the necessary number of wells and ultimately the schedule of drilling them.

Nevertheless, complicated models often grow out of experience with simple ones. Interpolation, for all its faults, may be a sensible starting point.

4.6.5 A Waterflood Prospect - Production Scenarios

As a second example, we look at a problem from McCray (1975), *Petroleum Evaluation and Economic Decisions*. He posed the problem of a waterflood prospect, where recoverable must be estimated and then one of four types of observed production schedules is followed to generate a revenue stream. The model combines volumetric estimates, prices, costs, and production scheduling. Moreover, there are several nice features of both spreadsheets and @RISK involved in the solution.

The overall objective is to estimate the Internal Rate of Return (IRR) for a waterflood project, given the following information about initial costs, operating costs, reservoir description, production schedules, prices, working interest, interest rate, and taxes. We solve the problem using McCray's original data (circa 1975) and assumptions in case you want to compare your solution to the one in the book.

Initial costs
$1,044,000
The fixed startup costs for 10 producers (300 ft depth), 30 injectors (3000 ft depth), 6 supply wells (1000 ft depth), surface lines (6000 ft of 4 in., 8000 ft of 2 in), a plant, and the lease.

Reservoir description
We know the area of the waterflood prospect because of primary production. We need to estimate the pay thickness and porosity because of variations recorded at the well penetrations. Recovery (factor) is estimated based on other waterflood data for similar reservoirs.

Area	fixed at 500 ac
Net pay	uniform: 10 to 20 ft,
Porosity	uniform: 12 to 22 %,
Recovery	uniform: 20 to 40 % of pore volume.

Annual costs	
Electricity for 102 hp of pumps	Fixed at $7140
Overhead for 25 wells	Uniform: $1000 to $2000
Labor	Uniform: $7200 to $14,400
Other data:	
price of crude	$3.00/STB
working interest	87.5 %
state tax	5 % on gross sales

Production schedules

Four equally likely production schedules are considered. We can think of these as a range from optimistic to pessimistic. In each case, first production is not achieved until the end of the third year.

Production Schedules Cumulative Fraction of Recovery

Year	Type1	Type2	Type3	Type4
1	0	0	0	0
2	0	0	0	0
3	0	0	0	0
4	0.04	0.04	0.03	0.03
5	0.17	0.13	0.12	0.1
6	0.35	0.24	0.22	0.19
7	0.56	0.42	0.35	0.29
8	0.73	0.6	0.5	0.42
9	0.85	0.73	0.62	0.53
10	0.94	0.84	0.73	0.64
11	0.99	0.91	0.82	0.73
12	1	0.96	0.89	0.82
13		0.99	0.94	0.87
14		1	0.97	0.92
15			0.99	0.95
16			1	0.98
17				0.99
18				1

4.6.6 Worksheet Design for Waterflood Model

Retrieve FLOOD.XLS shown in Figure 4.11. The worksheet contains file documentation at the top, input variables and preliminary calculations in rows 10-16, and a table with three parts.

Figure 4.11 Waterflood Prospect Example - Production Economics Model

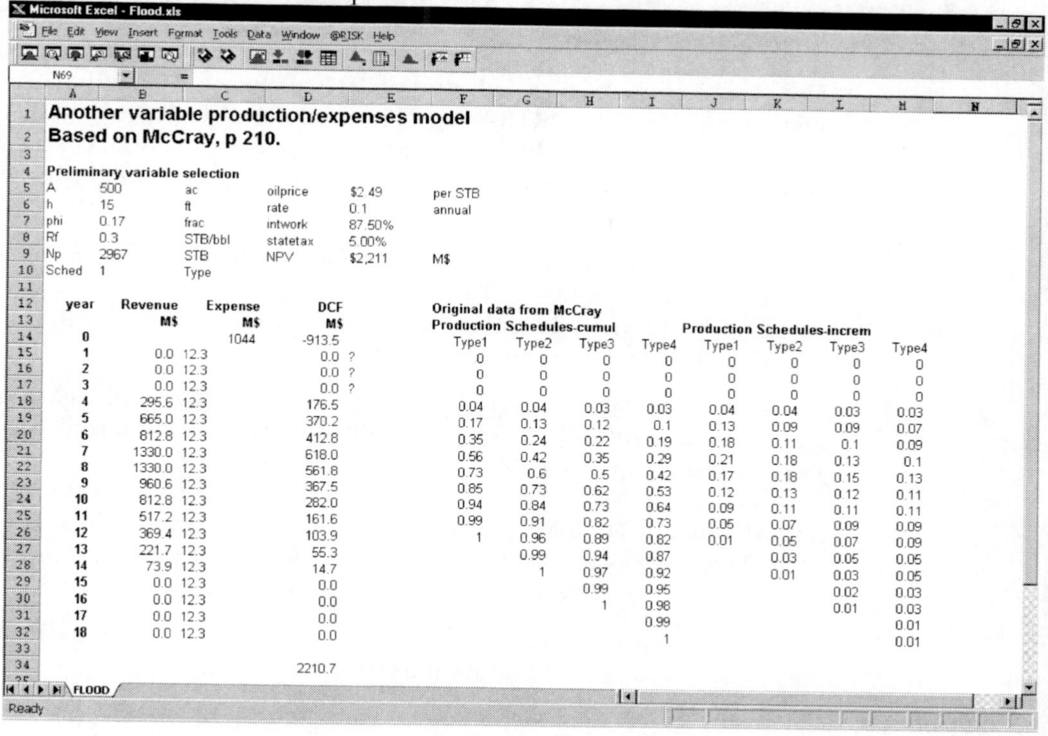

Microsoft Excel - Flood.xls

Another variable production/expenses model
Based on McCray, p 210.

Preliminary variable selection

A	500	ac	oilprice	$2.49	per STB
h	15	ft	rate	0.1	annual
phi	0.17	frac	intwork	87.50%	
Rf	0.3	STB/bbl	statetax	5.00%	
Np	2967	STB	NPV	$2,211	M$
Sched	1	Type			

Original data from McCray

year	Revenue M$	Expense M$	DCF M$		Type1	Type2	Type3	Type4	Type1	Type2	Type3	Type4
					\<Production Schedules-cumul\>				\<Production Schedules-increm\>			
0		1044	-913.5		0	0	0	0	0	0	0	0
1	0.0	12.3	0.0 ?		0	0	0	0	0	0	0	0
2	0.0	12.3	0.0 ?		0	0	0	0	0	0	0	0
3	0.0	12.3	0.0 ?		0	0	0	0	0	0	0	0
4	295.6	12.3	176.5		0.04	0.04	0.03	0.03	0.04	0.04	0.03	0.03
5	665.0	12.3	370.2		0.17	0.13	0.12	0.1	0.13	0.09	0.09	0.07
6	812.8	12.3	412.8		0.35	0.24	0.22	0.19	0.18	0.11	0.1	0.09
7	1330.0	12.3	618.0		0.56	0.42	0.35	0.29	0.21	0.18	0.13	0.1
8	1330.0	12.3	561.8		0.73	0.6	0.5	0.42	0.17	0.18	0.15	0.13
9	960.6	12.3	367.5		0.85	0.73	0.62	0.53	0.12	0.13	0.12	0.11
10	812.8	12.3	282.0		0.94	0.84	0.73	0.64	0.09	0.11	0.11	0.11
11	517.2	12.3	161.6		0.99	0.91	0.82	0.73	0.05	0.07	0.09	0.09
12	369.4	12.3	103.9		1	0.96	0.89	0.82	0.01	0.05	0.07	0.09
13	221.7	12.3	55.3			0.99	0.94	0.87		0.03	0.05	0.05
14	73.9	12.3	14.7			1	0.97	0.92		0.01	0.03	0.05
15	0.0	12.3	0.0				0.99	0.95			0.03	0.05
16	0.0	12.3	0.0				1	0.98			0.02	0.03
17	0.0	12.3	0.0					0.99			0.01	0.03
18	0.0	12.3	0.0					1				0.01
			2210.7									0.01

We assigned the appropriate values or distributions to A, h, phi, Rf, Sched (=production schedule), oilprice, rate (=annual discount rate), intwork (=working interest), and state tax. We entered the appropriate formulas for Np.

The cumulative recovery production schedule above was entered in the range F15..I32, with appropriate headings. The corresponding positions in columns J-M calculate incremental annual fractional production, with formulas like

```
J24:    =F24 - F23
L31:    =H31 - H30
```

Cell B10 is named "Schedule" and contains the distribution function Discrete({1,2,3,4},{1,1,1,1}), which returns one of the integers 1,2,3,4. This number is used as the "offset" entry in the Excel formulas such as

```
B15:  =CHOOSE(SCHEDULE,J15,K15,L15,M15)*NP*OILPRICE
```

Column B calculates annual revenue by checking the value in B10 to determine the appropriate "offset" column (schedule), getting the annual production fraction, multiplying by the recoverable oil (Cell B15), and then multiplying by the price of oil (Cell E11).

Column C represents a uniform variable between $8200 and $16,400. This is consistent with the FORTRAN program solution in McCray's text, but appears to neglect the electrical power costs. McCray chooses an annual cost once and uses it throughout the production schedule, but he suggests it might be better to choose the value annually.

Finally, Column D reduces the revenue by multiplying by 0.95 (i.e., by 1-the value in Cell E8) to account for 5% state tax, subtracts the expenses, and divides by a factor to bring the dollars back to "present value." The sum in D40 and again in E15 represents Net Present Value.

The internal rate of return (IRR) is the discount rate that will yield a net present value of 0 for profit. To put it differently, the IRR will yield future net income equal to initial investment. To estimate IRR, we introduce SIMTABLE({0.10,0.20, 0.30}) in Cell E6, the discount rate. We set **#Simulations** to 3 to match our choice of three values in SIMTABLE: 10%, 20%, and 30%. When we examine the results in the @RISK - Results window, we can look for a trend in the NPV as a function of this interest rate.

Choose two Output Ranges: Np and NPV. We set **#Iterations** to 300 and, as mentioned earlier, set **#Simulations** to 3.

Alternative Production Scheduling Models

There are several approaches to modeling field production profiles. One method is to use a decline curve approach, assuming the field production behavior looks like an exponential (or hyperbolic) decline curve for a single well. McCray's method , of course, generalizes to any number of decline profiles. A third method is to construct a generic field profile, which includes three periods: ramp up, plateau, and decline. In some locations, people have estimated the length of time the plateau endures. One estimate for the North Sea suggested that each year on plateau, gas wells decline about 5% (of reserves) while oil reservoirs deplete about 10% per year. A fourth method is to superimpose the decline curves for the individual wells. To do this, one needs to estimate the schedule of wells coming on line and the time to abandonment.

In general, production profile modeling, like investment scheduling, can get complex.

4.6.7 Exercises

1. In the @RISK - Results window, examine the individual simulations for NPV by right-clicking on NPV in the Explorer and selecting to graph results for each simulation. What shape of a distribution do you get for NPV? Explain.

2. Experiment with the SIMTABLE values until you bracket the IRR. How else might you estimate IRR? Of course, you could use trial and error. This worksheet is small enough that simulations should run quickly, allowing you to narrow down the range with suitable estimates in two or three passes. You could also use the Excel IRR, but you should be careful using IRR in a simulation model because it does not always return a value.

3. Discuss each of the following possible changes and ways to modify the worksheet:

   a) vary electrical costs,

   b) begin expenses in year 1, and

   c) assign both income and expenses to mid-year instead of end-of year.

What other changes might you suggest, based on your experience?

4. List all pairs of variables in the waterflood model that you think might be correlated. In each case, guess at the magnitude (and sign) of the correlation coefficient. Do you think you could find any data for these variables that could be used to estimate the correlation coefficient?

Bibliography

A few of the following articles and books were referenced. This list, while neither complete nor homogeneous, is offered to suggest further reading in risk analysis. Books on probability and statistics are best found by talking with someone who currently teaches the subjects. Alternatively, one can roam around in university bookstores to see the latest popular editions.

@RISK - Risk Analysis and Simulation add-in for Microsoft Excel, Release 4.0 User's Guide, Palisade Corp., Newfield NY, 2000.

Aitchison, J. and Brown, J.A.C, *The Lognormal Distribution*, Cambridge University Press, 1957.

Baker, R.A.: "When is A Prospect or Play Played Out?" *Oil and Gas Journal*, Jan. 11, 1988, p.77-80.

Behrenbruch, P. et al.: "Uncertainty and Risk in Petroleum Exploration and Development: The Expectation Curve Method," paper SPE 19475 presented at the 1989 Asia-Pacific Conference in Sydney, 13-15 Sept.

BestFit - Distribution Fitting Software for Windows, Release 4.0, Palisade Corp., Newfield NY, 2000.

Caldwell, R.H. and Heather, D.I.: "How To Evaluate Hard-To-Evaluate Reserves," *JPT*, Aug 1991, p. 998-1003.

Clemen, R.T., *Making Hard Decisions - An Introduction to Decision Analysis*, PWS-Kent Publishing, Boston, 1991.

Cronquist, C.: "Reserves and Probabilities -- Synergism or Anachronism?," *JPT*, Oct. 1991, p 1258-1264.

Damsleth, E. and Hage, A.: "Maximum Information at Minimum Cost: A North Sea Field Development Study Using Experimental Design," paper SPE 23139 presented at the 1991 Offshore Europe Conference, Aberdeen.

Davies, G.G. and Whiteside, M.W.: "An Integrated Approach to Prospect Evaluation," paper 23157 presented at the 1991 Offshore Europe Conference, Aberdeen.

Dhir, R., Dern, R.R. and Mavor, M.J.: "Economic and reserve Evaluation of Coalbed Methane Reservoirs," JPT, Dec. 1991, 1424-1431, 1518.

Drew, L.J., *Oil and Gas Forecasting - Reflections of a Petroleum Geologist*, Oxford University Press, New York, 1990.

Feller, W., *An Introduction to Probability Theory and ite Applications*, Vol I (1968, third ed.) and Vol II (1966), John Wiley, New York..

Harrell, J.A. "The Analysis of Bivariate Association" in *Use and Abuse of Statistical Methods in the Earth Sciences*, William B. Size, ed., Oxford, 1987.

Hertz, D. B., "Risk Analysis in Capital Investments", *Harvard Business Review*, Jan.-Feb. 1964, p. 95-106.

Hogg, R.V. and Craig, A.T., *Introduction to Mathematical Stsatistics*, (1965, 2nd ed.) Macmillan, New York.

Holtz, M.H.: "Estimating Oil Reserve Variability by Combining Geologic and Engineering Parameters," paper SPE 25827, presented at the 1993 SPE Hydrocarbon Economics and Evaluation Symposium, Dallas, Mar. 29-30.

Howard, R. A.: "Decision Analysis: Practice and Promise," *Management Science, 34,* 679-695.

McCray, A.W., Petroleum Evaluations and Economic Decisions, Prentice-Hall, Inc., Englewood Cliffs, NJ, 1975.

Megill, R.E., ed., *Evaluating & Managing Risk* - A Collection of Readings, SciData Publishing, Tulsa, 1985.

Megill, R.E., *An Introduction to Risk Analysis*, Petroleum Publishing Co, Tulsa, 1977.

Murtha, J.A.: "Infill Drilling in the Clinton: Monte Carlo Techniques Applied to the Material Balance Equation," paper SPE 17068 presented at the 1987 Eastern Regional Meeting, Pittsburgh, 21-23 Oct.

Murtha, J.A.: "Incorporating Historical Data in Monte Carlo Simulation," paper SPE 26245 presented at the 1993 Petroleum Computer Conference, New Orleans, July 11-14.

National Petroleum Council, "Enhanced Oil Recovery," 1984.

Newendorp, P., *Decision Analysis for Petroleum Exploration*, Pennwell, Tulsa, 1975.

Quick, A.N. and Buck, N.A., *Strategic Planning for Exploration Management*, IHRDC, Boston, 1983.

Shivers, R.M. and Domangue, R.J.: "Operational Decision Making for Stuck Pipe Incidents of the Gulf of Mexico: A Risk Economics Approach," paper SPE 21998, presented at the 1991 SPE/IADC Drilling Conference, Amsterdam, 11-14 Mar.

Smith, M.B.: "Probability Estimates for Petroleum Drilling Decisions," *JPT*, June 1974.

Spouge, J.R.: "CRAS: Computerized Prediction of Ship-Platform Collision Risks," SPE Paper 23154, presented at the 1991 Offshore Europe Conference, Aberdeen.

Walstrom, J.E., Mueller, T.D., and McFarlane, R.C.: "Evaluating Uncertainty in Engineering Calculations," *JPT* Dec. 1967, p.1595

Index